COLDPLAY
Play-Along Chord Songbook

WISE PUBLICATIONS
part of The Music Sales Group
London / New York / Paris / Sydney / Copenhagen / Madrid / Tokyo

Published by
Wise Publications
8/9 Frith Street, London WID 3JB, England.

Exclusive Distributors:
Music Sales Limited
Distribution Centre, Newmarket Road, Bury St Edmunds, Suffolk IP33 3YB, England.
Music Sales Pty Limited
120 Rothschild Avenue, Rosebery, NSW 2018, Australia.

Order No. AM85150
ISBN 0-7119-2693-X
This book © Copyright 2004 by Wise Publications.

CD recorded, mixed and mastered by Jonas Persson.
Backing vocals by Jo Edwards.
Piano by Paul Honey.
Guitars by Arthur Dick.
Bass by Paul Townsend.
Drums by Brett Morgan.
Printed in the United Kingdom by Caligraving Limited, Thetford, Norfolk.

Your Guarantee of Quality
As publishers, we strive to produce every book
to the highest commercial standards.
This book has been carefully designed to minimise awkward
page turns and to make playing from it a real pleasure.
Particular care has been given to specifying acid-free,
neutral-sized paper made from pulps which have not been
elemental chlorine bleached. This pulp is from farmed sustainable
forests and was produced with special regard for the environment.
Throughout, the printing and binding have been planned to
ensure a sturdy, attractive publication which should give years
of enjoyment. If your copy fails to meet our high standards,
please inform us and we will gladly replace it.

www.musicsales.com

Relative Tuning

The guitar can be tuned with the aid of pitch pipes or dedicated electronic guitar tuners which are available through your local music dealer. If you do not have a tuning device, you can use relative tuning. Estimate the pitch of the 6th string as near as possible to E or at least a comfortable pitch (not too high, as you might break other strings in tuning up). Then, while checking the various positions on the diagram, place a finger from your left hand on the:

5th fret of the E or 6th string and **tune the open A** (or 5th string) to the note (A)

5th fret of the A or 5th string and **tune the open D** (or 4th string) to the note (D)

5th fret of the D or 4th string and **tune the open G** (or 3rd string) to the note (G)

4th fret of the G or 3rd string and **tune the open B** (or 2nd string) to the note (B)

5th fret of the B or 2nd string and **tune the open E** (or 1st string) to the note (E)

E   A   D   G   B   E
or   or   or   or   or   or
6th 5th 4th 3rd 2nd 1st

Head

Nut

1st Fret

2nd Fret

3rd Fret

4th Fret

5th Fret

Reading Chord Boxes

Chord boxes are diagrams of the guitar neck viewed head upwards, face on as illustrated. The top horizontal line is the nut, unless a higher fret number is indicated, the others are the frets.

The vertical lines are the strings, starting from E (or 6th) on the left to E (or 1st) on the right.

The black dots indicate where to place your fingers.

Strings marked with an O are played open, not fretted. Strings marked with an X should not be played.

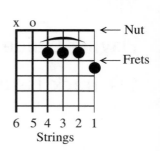

The curved bracket indicates a 'barre' - hold down the strings under the bracket with your first finger, using your other fingers to fret the remaining notes.

4

Amsterdam

Words & Music by
Guy Berryman, Jon Buckland, Will Champion & Chris Martin

D   A   Esus4   G   E   Gmaj7   Eadd9   G6

Capo first fret

Intro | D   A | Esus4 E G | D   A | Esus4 E G |

| D   A | Esus4 E G | D   A | E   G ||

Verse 1
D   A   Esus4 E   G
Come on,   oh my   star is fading,

D   A   Esus4 E   G
And I   swerve out   of control.

D   A   Esus4 E   G
If I'd,   if I'd   only waited,

D   A   E   G
I'd not be stuck here in this   hole. —

Link 1 | D   A | Esus4 E G | D   A | Esus4 E G |

Verse 2
D   A   Esus4 E   G
Come here,   oh my   star is fading,

D   A   Esus4 E   G
And I   swerve out   of control

D   A   Esus4 E   G
And I   swear, I wait - ed and waited.

D   A   E   G
I've got to get out of this   hole. —

Chorus 1
Eadd9   Gmaj7
But time is on your side,

               D   A
It's on your side   now.

          Eadd9
Not pushing you down,

      Gmaj7
And all around

     D   A
It's no cause for concern.

Instrumental 1 | D   A | Esus4   E   G | D   A | Esus4   E   G |

| D   A | Esus4   E   G | D   A | E $\frown$ G   ‖

Verse 3

D   A   Esus4   E   G
Come on,   oh my   star is fading,

D   A   Esus4   E   G
And I   see no chance of release.

D   A   Esus4   E   G
And I know I'm dead   on the surface

D   A   Esus4   E   G
But I am screaming under-neath. —

Chorus 2

Eadd9   Gmaj7
And time is on your side,

            D   A
It's on your side   now.

             Eadd9
Not pushing you down,

         Gmaj7
And all around

        D   A
No it's no cause for concern.

Instrumental 2 | Eadd9 | Gmaj7   G6 | D | A |

| Eadd9 | Gmaj7   G6 | D   A ‖

Chorus 2

            E   Gmaj7
Stuck on the end   of this ball and chain

             D   A
And I'm on my way   back down   yeah.

          E   Gmaj7
Stood on the edge,   tied to the noose,

        D   A
Sick to the stomach.

              E
You can say what you mean,

            Gmaj7
But it won't change a thing

cont.

          D   **A**
I'm sick of our se - crets.

          E   **Gmaj⁷**
Stood on the edge, tied to the noose

                  D   **A**   **Eadd⁹**
And you came along,   and you cut me loose.

Gmaj⁷   **D**   **A**   **Eadd⁹**
You came along   and you cut me loose.

Gmaj⁷   **D**   **A**
You came along   and you cut me loose.

Clocks

Words & Music by
Guy Berryman, Jon Buckland, Will Champion & Chris Martin

D   Am   Em   Amadd¹¹   Am⁷

Em⁷   Em/G   Fmaj⁷   C   G⁶   Fmaj⁹

Capo first fret

Intro

‖: D | Am | Am | Em :‖

‖: D | Am | Am | Em :‖

Verse 1

    D   **Amadd¹¹**
The lights go out and I can't be saved,
       Em⁷
Tides that I tried to swim against
    D   **Amadd¹¹**
Have brought me down upon my knees,
     Em⁷
Oh, I beg, I beg and plead,
     D   **Amadd¹¹**
Singing; come out with things unsaid,
     Em⁷
Shoot an apple off my head
   D   **Amadd¹¹**
And a trouble that can't be named
     Em⁷
A tiger's waiting to be tamed singing . . .

Chorus 1

D | **Am** | **Am** | **Em**
You ——————————— are,
D | **Am** | **Am** | **Em**
You ——————————— are.

Piano Riff 1

‖: D | Am | Am | Em :‖

Verse 2

   D   **Amadd11**
Confusion that never stops,

                   Em7
The closing walls and ticking clocks

       D   **Amadd11**
Gonna   come back and take you home

             Em7
I could not stop that you now know,

       D   **Amadd11**
Singing;   come out upon my seas,

             Em7
Cursed missed opportunities

     D   **Amadd11**
Am I   a part of the cure,

           Em7
Or am I part of the disease? Singing . . .

Chorus 2

D   │**Am**   │**Am**   │**Em**
You _____ are,

D   │**Am**   │**Am**   │**Em**
You _____ are.

D   │**Am**   │**Am**   │**Em**
You _____ are,

D   │**Am**   │**Am**   │**Em**
You _____ are.

Instrumental ‖: **D**   │**Am7**   │**Am7**   │**Em/G** :‖

  ‖: **D**   │**Am7**   │**Am7**   │**Em/G** :‖
    You _____ are.

Bridge

Fmaj7   **C**   **G6**
   And nothing else compares

Fmaj7   **C**   **G6**
   Oh no nothing else compares,

Fmaj7   **C**   **G6**   **Fmaj7** **Fmaj9** **Fmaj7** **Fmaj9**
   And nothing else compares.

Piano riff 2 ‖: **D**   │**Am**   │**Am**   │**Em**   :‖

  ‖: **D**   │**Am7**   │**Am7**   │**Em/G** :‖

Chorus 3

    D   **Am⁷**   **Em/G**
    You ——— are,

    D   **Am⁷**   **Em/G**
    You ——— are.

Outro

‖: **D**   **Am⁷**   **Em/G**
    Home, home, where I wanted to go.

D   **Am⁷**   **Em/G**
Home, home, where I wanted to go. :‖   *Repeat to fade*

Don't Panic

Words & Music by
Guy Berryman, Jon Buckland, Will Champion & Chris Martin

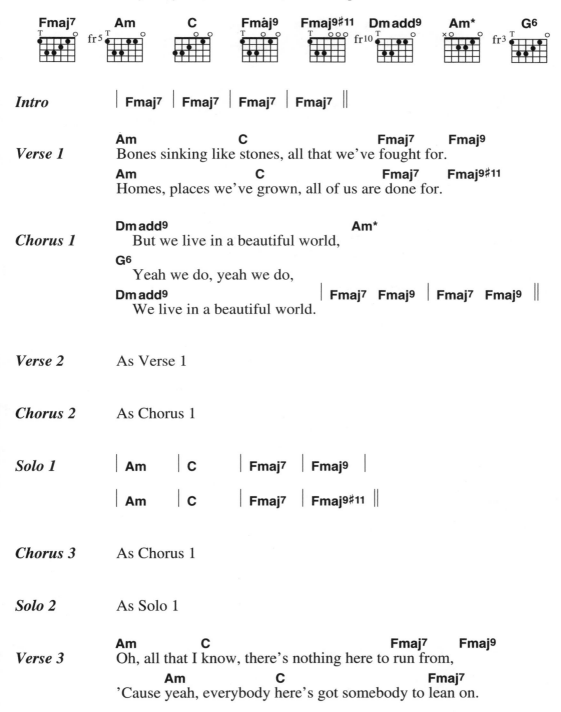

Intro | Fmaj⁷ | Fmaj⁷ | Fmaj⁷ | Fmaj⁷ ||

Verse 1
$$Am \qquad\qquad C \qquad\qquad\qquad\qquad Fmaj^7 \quad Fmaj^9$$
Bones sinking like stones, all that we've fought for.
$$Am \qquad\qquad C \qquad\qquad\qquad Fmaj^7 \quad Fmaj^{9\sharp 11}$$
Homes, places we've grown, all of us are done for.

Chorus 1
$$Dm add^9 \qquad\qquad\qquad\qquad\qquad Am^*$$
But we live in a beautiful world,
$$G^6$$
Yeah we do, yeah we do,
$$Dm add^9 \qquad\qquad\qquad\quad | Fmaj^7 \quad Fmaj^9 | Fmaj^7 \quad Fmaj^9 ||$$
We live in a beautiful world.

Verse 2   As Verse 1

Chorus 2   As Chorus 1

Solo 1 | Am | C | Fmaj⁷ | Fmaj⁹ |

| Am | C | Fmaj⁷ | Fmaj⁹ꜛ¹¹ ||

Chorus 3   As Chorus 1

Solo 2   As Solo 1

Verse 3
$$Am \qquad C \qquad\qquad\qquad\qquad\qquad\qquad Fmaj^7 \quad Fmaj^9$$
Oh, all that I know, there's nothing here to run from,
$$Am \qquad\qquad C \qquad\qquad\qquad\qquad Fmaj^7$$
'Cause yeah, everybody here's got somebody to lean on.

Everything's Not Lost

Words & Music by
Guy Berryman, Jon Buckland, Will Champion & Chris Martin

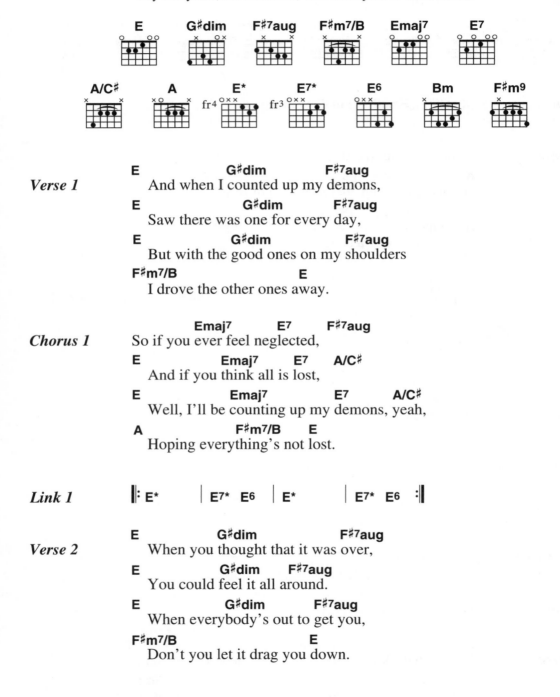

Verse 1

    E   G♯dim   F♯7aug
And when I counted up my demons,

    E   G♯dim   F♯7aug
Saw there was one for every day,

    E   G♯dim   F♯7aug
But with the good ones on my shoulders

F♯m7/B   E
I drove the other ones away.

Chorus 1

           Emaj7   E7   F♯7aug
So if you ever feel neglected,

    E   Emaj7   E7   A/C♯
And if you think all is lost,

    E   Emaj7   E7   A/C♯
Well, I'll be counting up my demons, yeah,

    A   F♯m7/B   E
Hoping everything's not lost.

Link 1

‖: E* | E7* E6 | E* | E7* E6 :‖

Verse 2

    E   G♯dim   F♯7aug
When you thought that it was over,

    E   G♯dim   F♯7aug
You could feel it all around.

    E   G♯dim   F♯7aug
When everybody's out to get you,

F♯m7/B   E
Don't you let it drag you down.

| *Chorus 2* | As Chorus 1 |

Link 2   ‖: **E*** | **E7*** **E6** | **E*** | **E7*** **E6** :‖

Chorus 3   As Chorus 1

                         E*   **E7*** **E6**

Outro   Singing out ah, ah ah yeah,   ah ah yeah,

E*   **E7*** **E6**   **E***
Ah ah yeah,   and everything's not lost,

                 E7* **E6**   **E***
So come on, yeah,   ah ah yeah,

               E7* **E6**   **E***
Come on, yeah,   and everything's not lost.

               E7* **E6**   **E***
Ah ah yeah,   ah ah yeah,

               E7* **E6**   **E***
Ah ah yeah,   and everything's not lost,

               E7* **E6**   **E***
Come on yeah,   ah ah yeah,

                   E7* **E6**
A-come on yeah.

E   **Bm**   **F♯m9**
  A-come on yeah,   ah ah yeah,

                         E
Come on yeah, and everything's not lost.

          Bm   **F♯m9**
Sing out yeah,   ah ah yeah,

                       E
Come on yeah, and everything's not lost.

          Bm   **F♯m9**
Come on yeah,   ah ah yeah,

                      E   **Bm** **F♯m9**
Sing out yeah, and everything's not lost.

God Put A Smile Upon Your Face

Words & Music by
Guy Berryman, Jon Buckland, Will Champion & Chris Martin

Db E6 Eb7 Dmaj7 Amaj7 F#add9

Tune down one and a half tones

Intro
| Db | E6 | Eb7 | Eb7 Dmaj7 |

| Db | E6 | Eb7 | Dmaj7 |

Verse 1
Db   E6   Eb7   Dmaj7
Where do we go, nobody knows!
Db   E6   Eb7   Dmaj7
I've gotta say I'm on my way ___ down.
Db   E6   Eb7   Dmaj7
God give me style and give me grace.
Db   E6   Eb7   Dmaj7
God put a smile upon my face. _____

Guitar Solo 1
| Db | E6 | Eb7 | Eb7 Dmaj7 |

| Db | E6 | Eb7 | Dmaj7 |

Verse 2
Db   E6   Eb7   Dmaj7
Where do we go to draw the line?
Db   E6   Eb7   Dmaj7
I've gotta say I've wasted all your time, honey, honey
Db   E6   Eb7   Dmaj7
Where do I go to fall from grace?
Db   E6   Eb7   Dmaj7
God put a smile upon your face. Yeah.

Chorus 1
Amaj7   E6   F#add9   Amaj7
And ah ___ when you work it out I'm worse than you. ___
                          E6   F#add9   Amaj7
Yeah, ___ when you work it out I wanted to. ___
                          E6   F#add9   Amaj7
And ah ___ when you work out where to draw the line, ___
                 E6   F#add9
Your guess is as good as mine.

Guitar Solo 2 | D♭ | E6 | E♭7 | E♭7   Dmaj7 |

                   | D♭ | E6 | E♭7 | Dmaj7   ‖

Verse 3

D♭   E6   E♭7   Dmaj7
     Where do we go nobody knows

D♭   E6   E♭7   Dmaj7
     Don't ever say you're on your way down   when

D♭   E6   E♭7   Dmaj7
     God gave you style and gave you grace,

D♭   E6   E♭7   Dmaj7
     And put a smile upon your face, oh yeah.

Chorus 2

       Amaj7   E6   F♯add9   Amaj7
And ah, when you work it out I'm worse than you. _____

                E6   F♯add9   Amaj7
Yeah, when you work it out I wanted to. _____

                E6   F♯add9   Amaj7
And ah, when you work out where to draw the line, _____

             E6   F♯add9   D♭   E6   E♭7
Your guess is as good as mine. _____

       Dmaj7   D♭   E6   E♭7
It's as good as mine. _____

       Dmaj7   D♭   E6   E♭7
It's as good as mine. _____

       Dmaj7   D♭   E6
It's as good as mine. _____

E♭7
Na na na na na na na na na na

       Dmaj7   Amaj7   E6
It's as good as mine. _____

F♯add9   Amaj7   E6
It's as good as mine. _____

F♯add9   Amaj7   E6   F♯add9
It's as good as mine. _____

Outro

D♭   E6   E♭7   Dmaj7
     Where do we go nobody knows

D♭   E6   E♭7   Dmaj7
     Don't ever say you're on your way down

     D♭   E6   E♭7   Dmaj7
When God gave you style and gave you grace

D♭   E6   E♭7   Dmaj7
     And put a smile upon your face.

Green Eyes

Words & Music by
Guy Berryman, Jon Buckland, Will Champion & Chris Martin

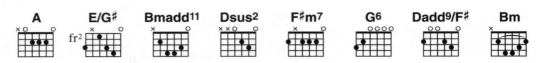

Verse 1

A   E/G#   Bmadd11
Honey you are a rock,

A   E/G#   Bmadd11
Upon which I stand.

A   E/G#   Bmadd11
And I come here to talk,

A   E/G#   Bmadd11
I hope you understand.

Verse 2

   Bmadd11
That Green Eyes,

    Dsus2
Yeah the spot light

    A E/G#
Shines upon you.

   Bmadd11   Dsus2
And how could anybody,

   A   E/G# F#m7
Deny you?

Chorus 1

Bmadd11   Dsus2
 I came here with a load,

        A G6   Dadd9/F#
And it feels so much light - er now I met you.

Bmadd11   Dsus2
 And honey you should know,

       A G6 Dsus2
That I could never go on without you.

Bmadd11 | Bmadd11 | Bmadd11 | Bmadd11 ‖
Green Eyes.

Verse 3

```
        A           E/G♯        Bmadd11
        Honey you    are the sea,
        A    E/G♯           Bmadd11
        Upon which I float.
        A        E/G♯          Bmadd11
        And I came here to talk
        A        E/G♯          Bmadd11
        I think you should know.
```

Verse 4

```
              Bmadd11
        That Green Eyes,
                  Dsus2             A       E/G♯
        You're the one that I wanted to find.
                  Bmadd11
        And any one who
                  Dsus2
        Tried to deny you
                            A       E/G♯  F♯m7
        Must be out of their minds.
```

Chorus 2

```
        Bmadd11                    Dsus2
          Because I came here with a load,
                            A  G6        Dadd9/F♯
        And it feels so much light - er since I met you.
        Bmadd11              Dsus2
          And honey you should know,
                            A   G6    Dsus2
        That I could never go on    without you.
        Bm
        Green Eyes,

        Green Eyes,
                A
        Oh oh oh.
                  Bm
        Oh oh oh.

        Oh oh oh.
```

Outro

```
        A           E/G♯        Bmadd11
          Honey you    are a rock
        A     E/G♯        Bmadd11
        Upon which I stand.
```

High Speed

Words & Music by
Guy Berryman, Jon Buckland, Will Champion & Chris Martin

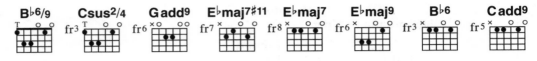

Tune guitar (from bottom string): D, G, D, G, B, D

Intro

‖: B♭6/9 | Csus2/4 | B♭6/9 | Csus2/4 :‖

| Gadd9 | Gadd9 | Gadd9 | Gadd9 ‖

Verse 1

E♭maj7#11   Gadd9   E♭maj7#11
Can anybody fly this thing?

Before my head explodes,
E♭maj7   E♭maj9 Gadd9
Before my head starts to ring.
E♭maj7   E♭maj9   Gadd9 B♭6
We've been living life   inside a bubble,
                            Cadd9 Gadd9
We've been living life inside a bubble.

Chorus 1

B♭6/9   Csus2/4
And confidence in you
               B♭6/9
Is confidence in me,
           Csus2/4 Gadd9
Is confidence in high   speed.

Verse 2

E♭maj7#11   Gadd9   E♭maj7#11
Can anybody stop this thing?

Before my head explodes,
E♭maj7   E♭maj9 Gadd9
Before my head starts to ring.
E♭maj7   E♭maj9   Gadd9 B♭6
We've been living life   inside a bubble,
                            Cadd9 Gadd9
We've been living life inside a bubble.

Chorus 2

B♭6/9   Csus2/4
    And confidence in you

                  B♭6/9
Is confidence in me,

               Csus2/4   Gadd9
Is confidence in high   speed,

In high speed, high speed.

Link

| Gadd9 | Gadd9 | Gadd9 | Gadd9   ‖

Outro

B♭6/9   Csus2/4   B♭6/9
    And high speed you want,

          Csus2/4   B♭6/9
High speed you want,

          Csus2/4   B♭6/9   Csus2/4
High speed you want,

                 Gadd9
High speed you want.

‖: Gadd9 | Gadd9   :‖ *Repeat to fade*

In My Place

Words & Music by
Guy Berryman, Jon Buckland, Will Champion & Chris Martin

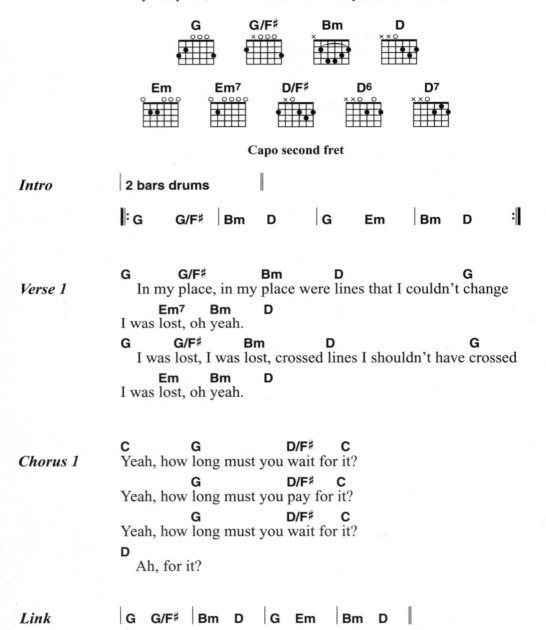

Capo second fret

Intro | 2 bars drums   ‖

‖: G   G/F♯ | Bm   D | G   Em | Bm   D :‖

Verse 1
G   G/F♯   Bm   D   G
   In my place, in my place were lines that I couldn't change
      Em⁷   Bm   D
I was lost, oh yeah.
G   G/F♯   Bm   D   G
   I was lost, I was lost, crossed lines I shouldn't have crossed
     Em   Bm   D
I was lost, oh yeah.

Chorus 1
C   G   D/F♯   C
   Yeah, how long must you wait for it?
     G   D/F♯   C
   Yeah, how long must you pay for it?
     G   D/F♯   C
   Yeah, how long must you wait for it?
D
   Ah, for it?

Link | G G/F♯ | Bm D | G Em | Bm D ‖

Verse 2

G G/F♯   Bm D   G
 I was scared, I was scared, tired and under-prepared,

   Em7 Bm D
But I'll wait for it.

G   G/F♯ Bm D   G
 And if you go, if you go and leave me down here on my own,

    Em Bm   D
Then I'll wait for you, yeah.

Chorus 2

C   G   D/F♯ C
Yeah, how long must you wait for it?

    G   D/F♯ C
Yeah, how long must you pay for it?

    G   D/F♯ C
Yeah, how long must you wait for it?

D
 Ah, for it?

Instrumental ‖: G G/F♯ | Bm D | G Em | Bm D   :‖

Middle

    G G/F♯ Bm
Singing: Please, please, please,

    D   G Em   Bm
Come back and sing to me, to me, ah me.

    D   G G/F♯ Bm
Come on and sing it out, now, now

    D   G Em Bm
Come on and sing it out, to me, me

    D
Come back and sing it.

Outro

G G/F♯   Bm   D   G
 In my place, in my place were lines that I couldn't change

    Em7 D6
I was lost, oh yeah.

D7 G
Oh yeah.

Politik

Words & Music by
Guy Berryman, Jon Buckland, Will Champion & Chris Martin

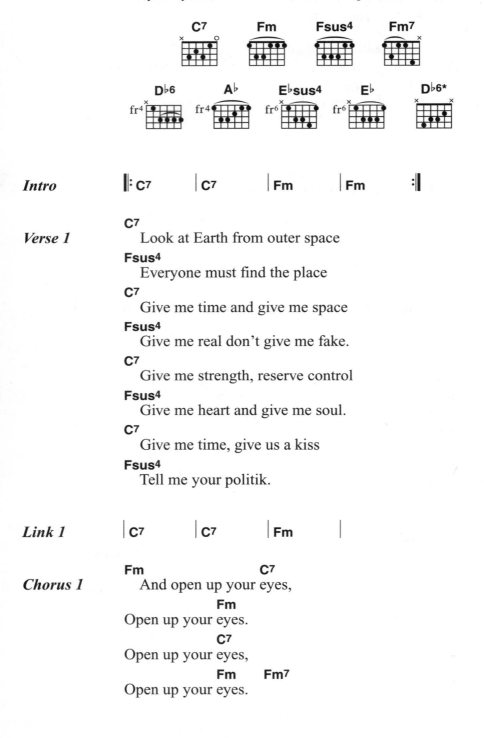

Intro   ‖: C7 | C7 | Fm | Fm   :‖

Verse 1

C7
Look at Earth from outer space
Fsus4
Everyone must find the place
C7
Give me time and give me space
Fsus4
Give me real don't give me fake.
C7
Give me strength, reserve control
Fsus4
Give me heart and give me soul.
C7
Give me time, give us a kiss
Fsus4
Tell me your politik.

Link 1 | C7 | C7 | Fm |

Chorus 1

Fm   C7
And open up your eyes,
           Fm
Open up your eyes.
           C7
Open up your eyes,
           Fm   Fm7
Open up your eyes.

Verse 2

C7
Give me one, 'cause one is best,

Fsus4
In confusion confidence

C7
Give me peace of mind, and trust

Fsus4
And don't forget the rest of us.

C7
Give me strength, reserve control

Fsus4
Give me heart and give me soul.

C7
Wounds that heal, and cracks that fix

Fsus4
Tell me your politik.

Chorus 2

           C7
And open up your eyes,

      Fm
Open up your eyes.

      C7
Open up your eyes,

      Fm
Open up your eyes.

 Fm7   **C7**
Just open up your (eyes.)

Link 2

| C7 | C7 | Fm | Fm | D♭6 | |

eyes.

| D♭6 | A♭ | A♭ | E♭sus4 | E♭ | ‖

Outro

Fm   **D♭6***   **A♭** **E♭sus4** **E♭** **Fm**
Give me love over, love over, love over this. Ah. _____

        D♭6*   **A♭**   **E♭sus4** **E♭**
Give me love over, love over, love over this. Ah, ah. _____

| Fm | Fm | D♭6* | D♭6* | A♭ | A♭ | |

| E♭sus4 | E♭ | Fm | Fm | D♭6* | D♭6* | |

| A♭ | A♭ | E♭sus4 | E♭ | Fm | ‖

23

A Rush Of Blood To The Head

Words & Music by
Guy Berryman, Jon Buckland, Will Champion & Chris Martin

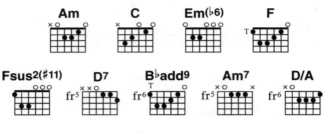

Tune guitar

⑥ = E   ③ = G
⑤ = A   ② = B
④ = D   ① = C

Verse 1

               Am   **C**

He said I'm gonna buy this place and burn it down,

Em(♭6)   **Am**

I'm gonna put it six feet underground.

                                                    C

He said I'm gonna buy this place and watch it fall

Em(♭6)   **Am**

Stand here beside me baby in the crumbling walls.

Verse 2

               Am   **C**

Oh I'm gonna buy this place and start a fire,

Em(♭6)   **Am**

Stand here until I fill all your heart's desires.

                                                      C

Because I'm gonna buy this place and see it burn

Em(♭6)   **Am** |**Am** |

Do back the things it did to you in return.

Link 1

               F   **Fsus2(♯11)**

Ha _ ha _____

               F   **Fsus2(♯11)**

Ha _ ha._____

Verse 3

         Am   **C**
He said I'm gonna buy a gun and start a war,
  Em(♭6)   **Am**
If you can tell me something worth fighting for.

Oh and I'm gonna buy this place, is what I say, **C**
 Em(♭6)   **Am** **Am** |
Blame it upon a rush of blood to the head.

Chorus 1

       F   **D7**
Honey, all the movements you're starting to make
                           F
See me crumble and fall on my face.

                         D7
And I know the mistakes that I've made,
   B♭add9   **F**
See it all disappear without a trace,
                    D7
And they call as they beckon you on,
    B♭add9   **(Am)**
They said start as you mean to go on.

| **Am** | **C** | **Em(♭6)** |

Am
 Start as you mean to go on.

| **Am** | **C** | **Em(♭6)** | **Am** |

Verse 4

       Am   **C**
He said I'm gonna buy this place and see it go,
  Em(♭6)   **Am**
Stand here beside my baby, watch the orange glow.

                         C
Some will laugh and some just sit and cry,
  Em(♭6)   **Am**
But you just sit down there and you wonder why.

Verse 5

       Am   **C**
So I'm gonna buy a gun and start a war,
Em(♭6)   **Am**
If you can tell me something worth fighting for.

                              C
Oh and I'm gonna buy this place, is what I say,
Em(♭6)   **Am**
Blame it upon a rush of blood to the head, oh to the head.

Chorus 2

         F   **D⁷**
Honey, all the movements you're starting to make

                          F
See me crumble and fall on my face.

                        D⁷
And I know the mistakes that I've made,

      B♭add⁹   **F**
See it all disappear without a trace,

                     D⁷
And they call as they beckon you on,

      B♭add⁹   **(Am)**
They said start as you mean to go on.

 Am   **C**   **Em(♭6)**
    As you mean to go on,

 Am
    As you mean to go on.

| **Am** | | **C** | | **Em(♭6)** | **Am** | |

Verse 6

 Am
   So meet me by the bridge,

             C
Oh meet me by the lake.

             Em(♭6)   **Am**
When am I gonna see that pretty face again?

Oh meet me on the road,

             C
Oh meet me where I ＿＿ said,

       Em(♭6)   **Am⁷**   **D/A**
Blame it all upon a rush of blood to the head.

Outro | **Am⁷** **D/A** | **Am⁷** **D/A** | **Am⁷** **D/A** | **Am** | ‖

26

The Scientist

Words & Music by
Guy Berryman, Jon Buckland, Will Champion & Chris Martin

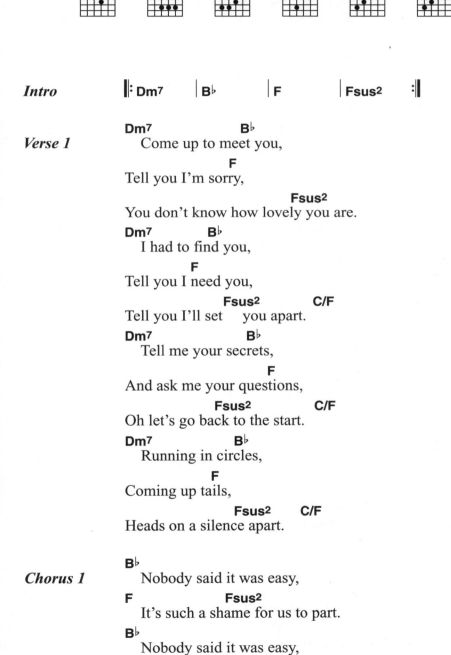

Intro   ‖: Dm7 | B♭ | F | Fsus2   :‖

Verse 1

Dm7   B♭
 Come up to meet you,

     F
Tell you I'm sorry,

        Fsus2
You don't know how lovely you are.

Dm7   B♭
 I had to find you,

     F
Tell you I need you,

      Fsus2   C/F
Tell you I'll set you apart.

Dm7   B♭
 Tell me your secrets,

       F
And ask me your questions,

     Fsus2   C/F
Oh let's go back to the start.

Dm7   B♭
 Running in circles,

     F
Coming up tails,

     Fsus2 C/F
Heads on a silence apart.

Chorus 1

B♭
 Nobody said it was easy,

F   Fsus2
 It's such a shame for us to part.

B♭
 Nobody said it was easy,

cont.

      F   **C/F**   **Fsus2**   **C**
No-one ever said it would be this hard.
   C/G   **(F)**
Oh, take me back to the start.

Link | **F** | **B♭** | **F** | **F** | **F** | **B♭** | **F** | **Fsus2** ‖

Verse 2

   Dm7   **B♭**
I was just guessing
                     F
At numbers and figures,
                Fsus2
Pulling your puzzles apart.
   Dm7   **B♭**
Questions of science,
                   F
Science and progress,
                Fsus2
Do not speak as loud   as my heart.
   Dm7   **B♭**
Tell me you love me,
                   F
Come back and haunt   me,
               Fsus2
Oh and I rush to the start.
   Dm7   **B♭**
Running in circles,
                 F
Chasing our tails,
               Fsus2
Coming back as we are.

Chorus 2

   B♭
Nobody said it was easy,
   F   **Fsus2**
Oh it's such a shame for us to part.
   B♭
Nobody said it was easy,
   F   **C/F**   **Fsus2**   **C**
No-one ever said it would be so hard.
   C/G   **(F)**
I'm going back to the start.

Instrumental | **F** | **B♭** | **F** | **F** | **Dm7** | **B♭** | **F** | **F**   ‖

Outro

Dm7   **B♭**   **F** | **F** |
  Ooh _____

Dm7   **B♭**   **F** | **F** |
  Ah ooh _____

Dm7   **B♭**   **F** | **F** |
  Oh ooh _____

Dm7   **B♭** $\widehat{\textbf{F}}$
  Oh ooh.

Sparks

Words & Music by
Guy Berryman, Jon Buckland, Will Champion & Chris Martin

Em7   Em(maj9)   Em7*   G9   D♭dim

Cmaj9   Gmaj7   Amadd9/11   G   Em(maj7)

Capo sixth fret, tune top string down to D

Intro
| Em7* Em(maj9) | Em7* G9 | D♭dim | Cmaj7 |

‖: Gmaj7 | Em7* | Gmaj7 | Em7* :‖

Verse 1

Gmaj7   Em7*   Gmaj7
    Did I drive you away?

                               Em7*
Well I know what you'll say,

          Amadd9/11   Gmaj7   G
You'll say "Oh, sing one you know."

Gmaj7   Em7*   Gmaj7
    But I promise you this,

          Em7   Amadd9/11
I'll always look out for you,

                    Gmaj7
That's what I'll do.

Bridge 1

          Em7   Em(maj9) | Em7* G9 | D♭dim | Cmaj9 |
Say I, _____

                 Em7   Em(maj9) | Em7* G9 | D♭dim | Cmaj9 ‖
And say I. _____

Link 1
‖: Gmaj7 | Em7* | Gmaj7 | Em7* :‖

Verse 2

Gmaj⁷   **Em⁷* Gmaj⁷**
    My heart is yours,
                 Em⁷*   Amadd⁹/₁₁
It's you that I hold on to,
                 Gmaj⁷ G Gmaj⁷
That's what I do.

                          Em⁷* Em(maj⁷) Gmaj⁷
And I know I was wrong,
                 Em⁷
But I won't let you down.
Amadd⁹/₁₁   **Gmaj⁷ G**
Oh yeah, I will, yeah I will, yes I will.

Bridge 2

         Em⁷ Em(maj⁹) │ Em⁷* G⁹ │ D♭dim   │ Cmaj⁷   │
I said I, _____
         Em⁷ Em(maj⁹) │ Em⁷* G⁹ │ D♭dim   │ Cmaj⁷   ‖
I cry I. _____

Chorus

         Gmaj⁷   Em⁷*
And I saw sparks,
         Gmaj⁷   Em⁷*
Yeah I saw sparks,
      Gmaj⁷   Em⁷*
I saw sparks,
         Gmaj⁷   Em⁷*
Yeah I saw sparks,
      Gmaj⁷
See me now.

Coda

         Em⁷* Gmaj⁷
La la la, la oh,
         Em⁷* Gmaj⁷
La la la, la oh,
         Em⁷* Gmaj⁷
La la la, la oh,
         Em⁷* Gmaj⁷
La la la, la oh.

Trouble

Words & Music by
Guy Berryman, Jon Buckland, Will Champion & Chris Martin

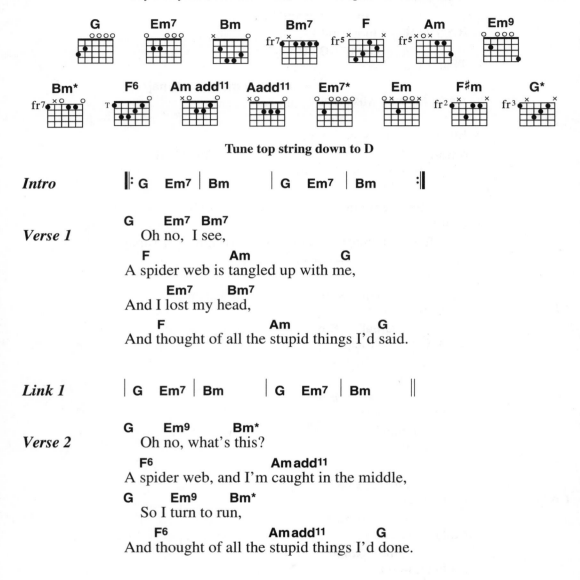

Tune top string down to D

Intro   ‖: G   Em⁷ │ Bm   │ G   Em⁷ │ Bm   :‖

Verse 1

  G Em⁷ Bm⁷
  Oh no, I see,

   F   Am   G
 A spider web is tangled up with me,

   Em⁷   Bm⁷
 And I lost my head,

    F   Am   G
 And thought of all the stupid things I'd said.

Link 1   │ G   Em⁷ │ Bm   │ G   Em⁷ │ Bm   ‖

Verse 2

  G Em⁹ Bm*
  Oh no, what's this?

   F⁶   Am add¹¹
 A spider web, and I'm caught in the middle,

  G Em⁹ Bm*
  So I turn to run,

   F⁶   Am add¹¹   G
 And thought of all the stupid things I'd done.

Chorus 1

             Aadd11   **Em7**
And ah, I never meant to cause you trouble,
             Aadd11   **Em7**
And ah, I never meant to do you wrong,
             Aadd11   **Em7**
And ah, well if I ever caused you trouble,
             Aadd11   **Em7**
Then oh, I never meant to do you harm.

Link 2 | **G** **Em7** | **Bm** | **G** **Em7** | **Bm** ||

Verse 3

G   **Em9** **Bm***
  Oh no, I see,
F6   **Amadd11**
A spider web and it's me in the middle,
G   **Em7**   **Bm***
  So I twist and turn,
   F6   **Amadd11**   **G**
But here I am in my little bubble.

Chorus 2

              Aadd11   **Em7**
Singing out ah, I never meant to cause you trouble,
             Aadd11   **Em7**
And ah, I never meant to do you wrong,
             Aadd11   **Em7**
And ah, well if I ever caused you trouble,
             Aadd11   **Em7**
Then oh no I never meant to do you harm.

Link 3 ||: **G** **Em9** | **Bm*** | **G** **Em9** | **Bm***   :||

Coda

Em   **F♯m**   **G*** **F♯m**   **Em**
  And they spun a web for me,
          F♯m   **G*** **F♯m**   **Em**
And they spun a web for me,
             F♯m   **G*** **F♯m** **Em** | **Em** |
And they spun a web for me.

      ||: **G** **Em7** | **Bm*** | **G** **Em7** | **Bm***   :||

Yellow

Words & Music by
Guy Berryman, Jon Buckland, Will Champion & Chris Martin

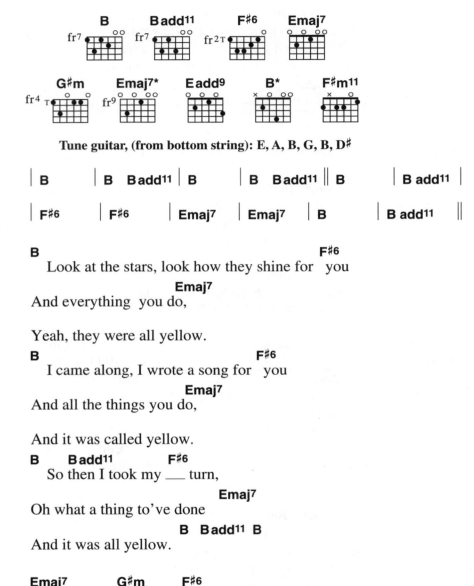

Tune guitar, (from bottom string): E, A, B, G, B, D♯

Intro | B | B   Badd¹¹ | B | B   Badd¹¹ ‖ B | B add¹¹ |

| F♯6 | F♯6 | Emaj⁷ | Emaj⁷ | B | B add¹¹ ‖

Verse 1

B   F♯6
  Look at the stars, look how they shine for   you
                       Emaj⁷
And everything you do,

Yeah, they were all yellow.
B   F♯6
  I came along, I wrote a song for   you
                Emaj⁷
And all the things you do,

And it was called yellow.
B   Badd¹¹   F♯6
  So then I took my __ turn,
                Emaj⁷
Oh what a thing to've done
              B   Badd¹¹ B
And it was all yellow.

Chorus 1

Emaj⁷   G♯m   F♯6
  Your skin,   oh yeah, your skin and bones
Emaj⁷* G♯m   F♯6
  Turn into something beautiful,
Emaj⁷   G♯m   F♯6   Emaj⁷
  'N'you know,   you know I love you so,
E add⁹
  You know I love you so.

Link 1 | B | B | F#6 | F#6 |

| Emaj7 | Emaj7 | B | B   ‖

Verse 2

B   F#6
   I swam across, I jumped across for   you,
                      Emaj7
Oh, what a thing to do

'Cause you were all yellow.
B   Badd11   F#6
   I drew a line, I drew a line for   you,
               Emaj7
Oh, what a thing to do
                B   Badd11   B
And it was all yellow.

Chorus 2

Emaj7   G#m   F#6
   Your skin,   oh yeah, your skin and bones
Emaj7*   G#m   F#6
   Turn into something beautiful,
Emaj7   G#m   F#6   Emaj7
 'N'you know?   For you I bleed myself dry,
Eadd9
   For you I bleed myself (dry.)

Link 2 | B | B | F#6 | F#6 |
dry.

| Emaj7 | Emaj7 | B | B   ‖

Coda

    B   F#6
It's true, look how they shine for you,
                 Emaj7
Look how they shine for you, look how they shine for,
B   F#6
   Look how they shine for you,
                 Emaj7
Look how they shine for you, look how they shine.
B*
   Look at the stars,
              F#madd11
Look how they shine for   you
             Emaj7
And all the things that you __ do.

Shiver

Words & Music by
Guy Berryman, Jon Buckland, Will Champion & Chris Martin

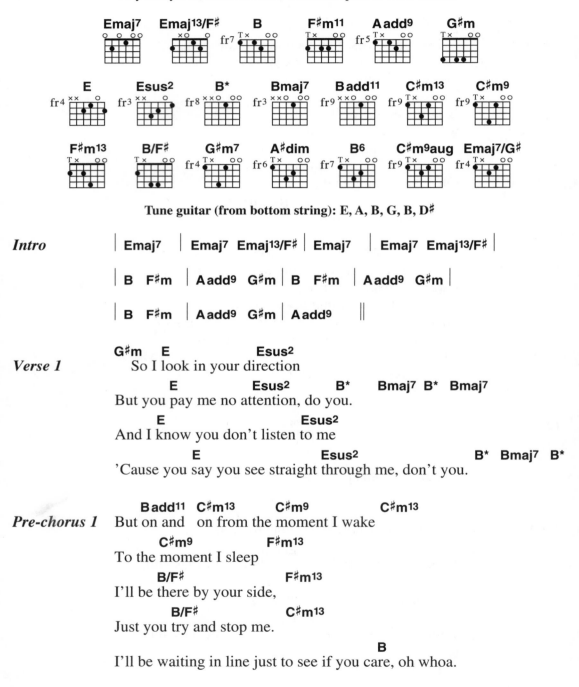

Tune guitar (from bottom string): E, A, B, G, B, D#

Intro

| Emaj7 | Emaj7 Emaj13/F# | Emaj7 | Emaj7 Emaj13/F# |

| B F#m | Aadd9 G#m | B F#m | Aadd9 G#m |

| B F#m | Aadd9 G#m | Aadd9 ‖

Verse 1

G#m   E   Esus2
So I look in your direction
        E   Esus2   B*   Bmaj7 B* Bmaj7
But you pay me no attention, do you.
        E   Esus2
And I know you don't listen to me
            E   Esus2   B* Bmaj7 B*
'Cause you say you see straight through me, don't you.

Pre-chorus 1

        Badd11 C#m13   C#m9   C#m13
But on and   on from the moment I wake
        C#m9   F#m13
To the moment I sleep
        B/F#   F#m13
I'll be there by your side,
            B/F#   C#m13
Just you try and stop me.
                                                    B
I'll be waiting in line just to see if you care, oh whoa.

cont.

G#m7   A#dim   B6
   Did you want me to change?

   A#dim
Well I'd change for good.

G#m7   A#dim   B6
   And I want you to know

           C#m9aug   B6
That you'll always get your way.

  A#dim   G#m7   Emaj7/G#
I wanted to say;

Chorus 1

                B F#m11 Aadd9 G#m
Don't you shiver,

       B6 F#m11 Aadd9 G#m
Shiver,

       B Aadd9   G#m7
Shiver,   ooh. _____

  Aadd9   G#m
I'll always be waiting for you.

Verse 2

       E   Esus2
So you know how much I need you

      E   Esus2   B*   Bmaj7 B* Bmaj7
But you never even see me, do you?

      E   Esus2 E   Esus2 B* Bmaj7 B*
And is this my final   chance of getting you?

Pre-chorus 2

   Badd11 C#m13   C#m9   C#m13
But on and on from the moment I wake

     C#m9   F#m13
To the moment I sleep

    B/F#   F#m13
I'll be there by your side,

    B/F#   C#m13
Just you try and stop me.

                        B
I'll be waiting in line just to see if you care, oh whoa.

G#m7   A#dim   B6
   Did you want me to change?

   A#dim
Well I'd change for good.

G#m7   A#dim   B6
   And I want you to know

          C#m9aug   B6
That you'll always get your way.

  A#dim   G#m7   Emaj7/G#
I wanted to say;

Chorus 2

Don't you shiver,

B6 F#m11 Aadd9 G#m

Shiver,

B Aadd9   G#m7

Shiver,   ooh. _____

Aadd9   G#m

I'll always be waiting for you.

| Emaj7 | Emaj7 | Emaj7   ‖

Bridge

B   Aadd9   Emaj7

Yeah, I'll always be waiting for you,

B   Aadd9   Emaj7

Yeah, I'll always be waiting for you,

B   Aadd9   Emaj7

Yeah, I'll always be waiting for you,

For you, I will always be waiting.

B   F#m11   Aadd9   G#m

And it's you I see but you don't see me,

B   F#m11   Aadd9   G#m

And it's you I hear so loud and clear.

B   F#m11   Aadd9   G#m

I sing it loud ___ and clear

Aadd9   G#m

And I'll always be waiting for you.

Verse 3

Emaj7   Esus2

So I look in your direction

Emaj7   Esus2

But you pay me no attention.

Emaj7   Esus2

And you know how much I need you

Emaj7   Esus2

But you never even see me.

If you like this book you will also like these...

Coldplay - A Rush Of Blood To The Head (TAB)
AM975128
Coldplay - A Rush Of Blood To The Head (PVG)
AM975139
Play Guitar With Coldplay
AM978098
Play Acoustic Guitar With Coldplay
AM978109

Coldplay – Parachutes (TAB)
AM968264
Coldplay - Parachutes (PVG)
AM970893
Play Piano With Coldplay
AM979132

CD Track Listing

1. Guitar Tuning
2. AMSTERDAM
   BMG Music Publishing Limited
3. CLOCKS
   BMG Music Publishing Limited
4. DON'T PANIC
   BMG Music Publishing Limited
5. EVERYTHING'S NOT LOST
   BMG Music Publishing Limited
6. GOD PUT A SMILE UPON YOUR FACE
   BMG Music Publishing Limited
7. GREEN EYES
   BMG Music Publishing Limited
8. HIGH SPEED
   BMG Music Publishing Limited
9. IN MY PLACE
   BMG Music Publishing Limited
10. POLITIK
    BMG Music Publishing Limited
11. A RUSH OF BLOOD TO THE HEAD
    BMG Music Publishing Limited
12. THE SCIENTIST
    BMG Music Publishing Limited
13. SPARKS
    BMG Music Publishing Limited
14. TROUBLE
    BMG Music Publishing Limited
15. YELLOW
    BMG Music Publishing Limited
16. SHIVER
    BMG Music Publishing Limited

MCPS

To remove your CD from the plastic sleeve, lift the small lip on the right to break the perforated flap. Replace the disc after use for convenient storage.

Lance did not want to hurt her, but the animal lust snarling within him was too powerful. He had to have this woman.

Winter Magic wrenched her mouth away. "*Kai,* Lance. Do not do this to me."

He clamped one hand around hers, then reached up and curved his fingers around her throat. . . . She glared hard at him. At first, she appeared angry, but after another moment her temper fell away. She looked as if she understood his pain—as if she, too, knew the need of a lost lover. . . .

Fire still raging through his body, he forced himself to relax. "It's just that it's been so damn long. And you're so beautiful."

He could not help himself. His lust jolted to life again. "Why do you have to be . . ." He lifted his head, then hesitated inches from her lips. "So damn beautiful?" Damn his lusting appetite. He could not stop himself. He found the back of her head and pulled her down to meet his crushing kiss. . . .

BELOVED WARRIOR

Deborah James

BERKLEY BOOKS, NEW YORK

BELOVED WARRIOR

A Berkley Book / published by arrangement with
the author

PRINTING HISTORY
Berkley edition / June 1993

ISBN: 0-425-13717-1

A BERKLEY BOOK ® TM 757,375
Berkley Books are published by The Berkley Publishing Group,
200 Madison Avenue, New York, New York 10016.
The name "BERKLEY" and the "B" logo
are trademarks belonging to Berkley Publishing Corporation.

PRINTED IN THE UNITED STATES OF AMERICA

10 9 8 7 6 5 4 3 2 1

To Popsaun—

For the countless hours of tireless storytelling when I was a child. For your wonderful knowledge of history and the love and pride you have passed on to me for Honey Lake Valley and the people who live there. I was listening . . .

Thanks, Dad, I Love You

Sharing is the greatest gift anyone can give—

With warmest affection, I thank my critique group— my friends: Jeannie, Meg, and Jamie for sharing their time, expertise, and opinions. You're the best.

To my editor, Melinda, who believed in my work and took a chance on me.

And as always to my husband, Jim, and my children for enduring the many months of my lack of sanity while I wrote this story. Thanks for hanging in there with me, guys.

1

California–Nevada Border
Late December 1875

Crouched on his haunches beneath a lone lodgepole pine, Lance Taggert cocked his head to the left so that his patched eye was somewhat protected from the dry winter wind. Bittersweet, the scent of home scurried across the sea of silver-green sagebrush, whistling its mournful welcome.

After ten long years, and even though he was still at least half a windy day away from the Triple-T, this desolate open range felt closer to heaven than anything he had known in a long time. His thoughts whirled backward, through his childhood memories.

His stomach cinched. There it was—that old coyote feeling. The one that left him uneasy and not knowing whether he should sing for joy or cry for himself. He had almost forgotten it. He shook his head. He had thought the barbs of those painful memories had been smoothed with time. God, how he hated returning to the family ranch under these conditions, but he simply had nowhere else to go.

Isolated on the hill's barren splendor, he tugged down his hat and watched a small band of mustangs below him nibble on sparse sprigs of grass that had cropped through the fresh blanket of snow. Flipping up his collar, he saw the lead mare prick her ears. She snorted, then led the herd off a few yards before stopping again.

What would it be like to see the old place again? Would it have changed much from what he remembered now that his father was dead and Eldon was in charge? At the thought of his older brother, he chuckled. Probably not. El was the spitting image of the old man—nail-hard, inflexible, and always right. And what about Shea, his younger brother? He had only been eleven when Lance had left home. What kind of man had he grown into?

A sudden hot breath rustled the back of his collar. Even before he turned his head, Lance knew he was in trouble. Cautiously he looked over his shoulder.

A large white stallion covered with black leopard spots stood directly behind him. The animal blew again and stomped the earth.

Lance swallowed. He had been so preoccupied with his reveries, he had not noticed the Appaloosa's approach. And now he had no chance of getting away. He had left the horse he had rented in Reno tied in a stand of pines edging the hill. He snatched a glimpse of the trees in the distance. Too far to make a run for it.

Shaking the flashing cascade of his mane, the animal backed off a couple of yards and circled Lance. As if challenging him to do battle, the horse stopped, flared his nostrils, and stomped a hole in the snow-covered ground.

Despite the near-freezing cold, Lance broke out in a sweat. He glanced at his surroundings. The lowest branches of the tree above him were too high to reach. He had nowhere to hide, nothing to burrow under, and only sagebrush to climb. His mind whirled. He had to try and soothe the stallion before it was too late. Aware that any sudden movement would startle the animal, he carefully stood. "Whoa, there, boy. Nothing to be afraid of here." He tried to sound comforting, though his heart beat a rampant pace.

For a moment it looked as though the stallion would yield his stand and settle down. But without warning he laid his ears back and shrieked. On legs seeming to be made of steel springs, he reared.

Staggering back a step, Lance braced himself for the attack. Akin to a war cry, a shrill blared above the Appaloosa's enraged scream. Out of the corner of his eye, Lance saw a movement.

A bulky shape, another horse, skidded in between Lance and the stallion in a flurry of white powder—but this one had a rider. She yelled something at him.

He did not quite understand. Unmistakably female, the woman's voice called out again. With an anxious expression she slumped her body to one side of her mount and reached out to him.

No time to think, barely time to act, Lance realized what she wanted him to do. He grabbed

her forearm and leapt up behind her astride the big
bay's rump.

One swift jab in the flanks by his rider and the
animal bolted. Nostrils distended, black mane flying, and tail straight out, the bay pummeled the
heavy-packed snow in a race for safety.

But the stallion continued his pursuit. Charging
them, he gnashed at the horse beneath Lance and
the woman, ripping out a small chunk of hide from
the animal's neck.

The woman screamed something Lance did not
understand. She kicked at the Appaloosa, almost
unseating herself.

Lance grabbed her waist, yanking her back
against him. Another mistake like that could cost
them both their lives. On impulse he reached under
her arms and snatched the reins out of her hands.
Grappling the bay's sides with his legs, he gripped
a thick lock of mane with one hand and yanked
back on the lead with the other.

Knee-deep in snow, the bay dug all fours into the
ground. But before they came to a complete stop,
Lance jerked the reins to the right. Forced to spin
around, the animal's eyes rolled back. Lance heeled
him hard. Despite the obviously painful wound
seeping blood down his neck, the big beast tore up
the snowpack with his long-legged strides.

After only a moment Lance chanced a look over
his shoulder. The stallion had given up the fight. He
eased up on the lead, and the bay slowed. "Whoa."

Even before the animal halted, the woman swung
one leg over the horse's head and leapt to the
ground.

Lance jumped down behind her. Still holding one

leather strap, he sucked in a replenishing breath and patted the bay's sweaty chest. Exhilarated, he shook his head and chuckled, then wheeled around to meet his savior. "That was one helluva ride, huh?"

Unblinking dark eyes spit black fire. "You took my horse!" She assaulted him in a guttural tongue.

He had not heard the language spoken by a woman since his wife so long ago. Taken back by both the clipped nasally undercurrent of her voice and her angry tone, Lance stared hard.

She threw back a single waist-length braid of blue-black hair. Garbed in a colorful Indian blanket coat, a man's white shirt, and blue jeans, she poised her slender body in a challenging posture—much as the Appaloosa had done moments ago. Glaring at him, her piercing expression held him warily entranced, yet strangely intrigued.

He caught a glimpse over her head of the Appaloosa standing eagle-watch with his harem in the distance. He looked back at the infuriated woman. The face-off was the same.

Sooner or later someone had to say something. Soothing words had not worked with the stallion; would they work with her? He smiled and pointed to the beadwork of her earbobs. Then lifting the reins, he gestured to the intricate weave of the horsehair hackamore. "Paiute, hmm?"

The woman glowered at him. She motioned toward the bay. "That is *my* horse."

Lance's brows shot upward. He had not expected her to have such command of English.

"Why did you take him from me?" she all but yelled.

"You almost fell—"

"No! I do not fall with *Kozo'koi tanowani* ever."

Still holding on to the reins, Lance glanced back at the panting bay. "Look, we could've both fallen." He cocked his head and squinted. "You know what that stallion would've done to us if we'd hit the ground?"

"I have known the Pogonip for a long time. He does not frighten me." She lifted a corner of her mouth in a taunting sneer. "It is you who was in trouble, *Ganoida bui*, not me."

Handsome eye? Lance flinched. He turned so that the injured side of his face was hidden from her view. After only three months since the failure of his surgery, it still made him uncomfortable to have people notice his eye—and they always did. He moved to the opposite side of the bay and checked the wound inflicted by the stallion. "What're you doing out here all alone?"

"I was tracking the *Pogonip puku'*."

Lance removed his bandanna, shook it out, and dabbed at the wound on the horse's neck. "That means White Death, doesn't it?"

"Horse of White Death," she corrected.

"Isn't that what your people call the fog—white death, I mean?"

She did not answer.

Did she understand? Maybe her English was not as good as he had first thought. He pointed out over the lower valley to the mist seeping up from the ground even now. But before he could question her further, she interrupted.

"It is the same. That is when the Pogonip comes

out. I have been trying to catch him for three days now."

Lance frowned at her. "Three days? Alone?"

"*Pisha*, alone."

"Do your people know you're out here by yourself?"

"They know. I can take care of myself."

"Like you just did?" Lance found himself becoming irritated.

"If I had not helped you, it would not have happened." Narrowing her eyes, she smiled, then gestured to the spot where the stallion had crept up behind him. "*I* was not the one caught in the open on foot."

Lance cut her a sharp gaze. The muscle beneath his patch began to throb. The woman had probably saved his life and he was grateful—but that did not mean he was willing to put up with her arrogance. "Look, I appreciate your help, but I've got to get home now."

She appeared to relax a bit, seemingly curious. Coming to face him across the horse's back, she tipped her head to one side and studied him. "You are a soldier?"

Lance shook his head. "Not since the war."

"War?"

"Between the states."

"Ah. When whites fought against themselves for the buffalo people."

"Buffalo people?"

"I do not remember how they are called." She rubbed her head briskly. "They have dark skin and hair like buffalo."

Lance grinned. "You mean Negroes?"

"That is the name."

He nodded. "Yes, not since then."

"If you are not a soldier, who are you?" Her large eyes reminded him of a squirrel peeking out at an intruder.

"My name's Lance."

"Ah. Lance." She gifted him with a small but obviously approving smile. "Why are you here? You go to Roops Fort?"

He wadded up the blood-splotched kerchief and shoved it into his jacket pocket, then moved around the animal to stand in front of her. "No. My home's near the hot springs there." He pointed behind her toward Honey Lake.

Her body tensed. Appearing suddenly frightened, she retreated a step. "You lie. I have never seen you before. I know all whites in this valley."

"I haven't been home for a long time."

"No. I would remember Ganoida bui." Panic filled her voice.

"Hey, wait a minute." Lance tried to calm her. "What's wrong?"

Her eyes darted fearfully around the landscape. "You are from the Taggert Ranch."

"Yeah." Lance shot her a puzzled stare. "How'd you know?"

At once she yanked a knife from the sheath strapped to her side. She lunged. The blade gleamed in the noonday sun, missing Lance's face by mere inches.

He stumbled backward. Another knife had cost him his vision. But before he could catch his balance, the woman leapt onto the bay. The animal pitched forward with a squeal.

Still holding the reins, Lance threw his arms up to halt the horse. Stiff-legged, the bay struck the ground just in front of him.

With a throaty snarl the woman all but ripped the reins from Lance's grasp. She dug her heels into the animal's flanks.

He lurched again, but Lance yanked down hard on the lead. "Whoa. Stop." He fought her gouging nails as she struck out at his face. "Damn it, woman—stop!" Ducking and dodging, he could not see her clearly. He found cloth and jerked. The fabric ripped.

The woman tumbled down on top of him. A heavy groan rushed from her throat. She tore at him like a wildcat—fury and blade attacking him with all her strength.

"That's enough!" Grabbing both of her wrists, Lance rolled her beneath him and straddled her middle. He leaned over so that his face hovered mere inches from hers. "That's enough!" he said with more force than before.

Chest heaving, hair freed from her braid webbing her flashing eyes, she glared up at him with a start.

"What the hell's wrong with you?" he asked between panting breaths. "You gone loco?"

Like someone insane, she shrieked. Pitching her body upward, she nearly unseated him from across her stomach.

"Stop it!" He slammed her hands into the snow, knocking the knife from her grasp. Their eyes met in a clash of wills. Lance caught sight of her ripped shirt. It exposed one tawny breast. Sweat beaded his face. Blood pounded in his temples—louder, and louder still—until the drumming became hoof-beats closing in around him. He looked up.

Less than twenty yards away a half-circle of horses pawed at the ground. Lance's gaze slid higher. His stomach tightened. The fear he had felt with the threat of the stallion could not compare to the panic that struck him now.

Astride each animal sat an angry-faced Indian. Each wore the same expression—an image of the woman's earlier blood-lust . . . and all were directed at him.

2

Winter Magic watched as the white man gazed up at the dozen warriors glowering down at him. Was it fear that registered in his expression? Maybe not, but the look of dread on his face could not be mistaken. Good. Now it was the Paiute's turn to wield the arm of strength and power.

The man rose carefully.

"You are hurt?"

She pushed herself up from the ground. Yanking her jacket closed over her torn shirt, she stepped back away from the one-eyed man and glanced at her uncle Nighthawk. She shook her head. "*Kai, Tunupiuts.*"

"Who is this one-eye?" Nighthawk asked.

"Lance Taggert," the man answered for himself.

Surprised, Winter Magic stared at the Ganoida bui. She had not expected him to know her people's language.

11

Strange. No one made a move toward him.

After a long moment of silence Nighthawk slid down from his paint's back. He walked over to stand in front of the white man. He appeared to be studying him.

Winter Magic, too, took stock of the man. He looked as though he had probably seen the passing of at least thirty seasons, maybe more. Tall and lean, his muscular thighs pressed the faded denim covering his legs. Her gaze rose past the heavy sheepskin coat. Trimmed in the usual style of the whites, yet longer than most, a thick shock of black-brown hair fell across his forehead to the edge of his brows. A thick curve of black whiskers covered his upper lip, adding a most unattractive feature to his stubbled face. She much preferred the smooth jaw of an Indian man.

Examining both ends of a scar that slashed just above and below his black patch like a chokecherry stain, she tried to avoid looking at his one visible eye. But it could not be helped. Disarmingly beautiful, its smoky-gray color beckoned her. It provoked in her the same dangerous exhilaration she felt whenever she challenged the teachings of her people and entered the mist of white death—the Pogonip that plagued the surrounding lands.

"You have changed much since last our meeting, Taggert." Nighthawk gestured to the shield covering the man's left eye.

"No more than you, Tunupiuts." The white man pointed to the leather chaps and regulation army hat on her uncle.

Nighthawk nodded. His black eyes lit with

laughter. Reaching out, he and the Ganoida bui clasped forearms.

Winter Magic stared in shock at the courteous exchange between the two men. Instead of taking the white man prisoner as she thought he should, Nighthawk had given his hand in friendship. "You know this man?"

Her uncle nodded. "He is a friend of my youth—"

"Friend?" she railed in her native tongue.

"A very good friend," the white man announced with a broad grin. "We kept each other out of a lot of trouble when we were kids."

"Mm. Is that how you remember it, Lance Taggert?"

"Well, maybe not exactly like that."

"Maybe *in* trouble is more honest?"

The Ganoida bui laughed a rich throaty chuckle. "Maybe."

Moving to where her knife lay in the snow, Winter Magic snatched it up. "The white is true to his youth still."

Nighthawk did not acknowledge her comment with even the slightest turn of his head in her direction. He released the Ganoida bui's hand. "Where have you been these long years past, old friend?"

"Uncle?" Winter Magic insisted. "You have no mask covering either of *your* eyes—did you not see what he did?"

Nighthawk shifted toward her. "I saw. You said you were not hurt."

Winter Magic's mouth fell open. She could not believe Nighthawk's lack of concern. "Uncle—"

"You do not know this man as I. He would not have harmed you."

She started to protest, but Nighthawk shook his head.

"Komeni Tu'madai, you are the daughter of my brother—the girl-child of my heart." He arched an understanding brow. "You forget . . . I know you well. You are like the snake that rattles—you rush at any movement, but do not see what it is you strike."

With angry strides she moved to within arm's distance of the white man. "Look at me, Uncle. You cannot let him go unpunished." She pointed at the Ganoida bui with a jab of the blade.

"Away with the knife." Nighthawk's usually subdued tone vanished with his gruff use of English.

"He attacked me, Uncle," she retorted in the white language. "I have the right to—"

"*I* attacked you?" The man glared at her. "*You* attacked me."

Nighthawk turned a scowl on her. "This is true?"

Winter Magic held her coat tightly over her chest. She fixed a defiant stare on the pale gray eye of the white man.

"This is true?" Nighthawk asked more forcefully than before.

Slowly Winter Magic's anger yielded to embarrassment. In the silence even the breathing of the horses sounded deafening. She lowered her gaze to the snow-covered ground.

With the death of her mother and father when she was but five, Nighthawk had stepped into the parental role and taken her into his own family.

Normally, she would never truly cross him, but this was different.

Taking a breath, she lifted an accusing stare to the white man. "Ganoida bui is from the Triple-T—worse, he himself clearly brags he is a Taggert. With everything they have done to us, is what you saw not enough, Uncle?"

"I know this man. If what he says is truth, he did no more than protect himself."

"But he is a Taggert—"

"As we are Indian. Would you have him hate us all?" He swept a hand toward the men sitting atop their restless ponies. "You surprise me, Komeni Tu'madai. You were of the first to condemn our treatment by the men at the Triple-T."

"But that was different."

"How?" Before she could answer, he held up a hand. "No quarrels now."

"If not now, when?" Winter Magic could not contain her temper. Even though he had chosen to leave the tribe in hopes of leading his people into a new way of life, her uncle was still one of the tribal leaders and still held much power. She knew she should remain silent, but her wounded pride would not allow her to back down. "We have worked hard for what we have. We cannot let men like this take it from us."

"You are quick to judge one you do not know, Komeni Tu'madai." With silent regard he frowned upon the unsheathed blade still grasped in her hand.

Knowing she should obey, but unwilling to submit, she held her ground.

Nighthawk shook his head again, an expression

of disapproval marking his features. "Two winters ago, when the government food did not come for us on the reservation and the bitter snows left us starving and cold, it was you who pushed us toward the whites' way of life. You who put forward the plan to the people for our own ranch."

"The whites challenge us for daring to take hold of our own lives," she interrupted. "They chase us down like animals. I was a fool to think it would work. We are not allowed the dignity to even try." Rage coursed through her blood. Never before had she spoken out in anger to her uncle. She thought of her cousin, Takes His Pants Off, and how only weeks before the men of the Taggert Ranch had caught him chasing mustangs. They had roped him and dragged him through the brush and cactus. He had lain out in the snow bleeding for half a day before he was found. "Have you forgotten *Kasawinaid* so quickly?"

"I have not forgotten. He knew the risks." Nighthawk offered her a disappointed smile. "You are no longer a child. Did you believe our test of strength would come easy?"

Winter Magic's face heated. In truth, she had— though deep down she knew that what Nighthawk said was correct. But why did he have to be so wise—especially now in front of the Ganoida bui? She cut the white man an insulting glance, but was met by one of equal—no, superior—distinction. An offensive inspection of her appearance.

His gaze boldly traveled the full length of her body before returning to her eyes.

He was no different than the other whites. The men at the Triple-T had looked at her in this same way. Always sneering and suggesting things with their stares. They saw nothing more than an Indian, a squaw to use for their hideous pleasures.

So that was how it was to be between her and the Ganoida bui. He thought to humiliate her. But could he play the game as well as she? She straightened her posture. She could prove to Nighthawk and the other men that this white was no friend to the Paiute.

She met his stare headlong. Then, with complete disregard of consequence, she freed her grasp on her coat and lowered her hands to her sides. Her eyes remained fixed on his. An icy wind blew open the torn fragments of her shirt. She felt its unmerciful bite, but remained steadfast. "This is Paiute pride, Ganoida bui. You cannot break me."

He deepened his stare, but did not stir.

Yet, inside, Winter Magic did. She had sought to humble him before her uncle and the men of her tribe, but it was *he* who now made *her* uncomfortable. She fought the urge to turn away.

"Komeni Tu'madai!" Her uncle's hand stung her cheek.

She flinched. Tears burned her eyes.

Arm still poised from his strike, Nighthawk glowered down at her. "You shame us!"

Slowly Winter Magic became aware of the uneasy faces turned on her. She felt the stubborn tilt in her chin give way to a disgraceful quiver.

"Cover yourself," Nighthawk commanded in their native tongue.

Humbling herself before him, she secured her clothing together and averted her eyes to her moccasins. Her vision blurred. "Forgive me, Uncle," she said, her voice faltering to a murmur.

"It is too late. Go. *Nanishtuhai*! Pray—repent your shame." He gestured to Mogu'pa kudakw, the distant mountains behind her. "Go to the hot springs. Do not return to us until you have cleansed your spirit."

Humiliated and shamed by both her uncle's discipline and her own unruly pride and lack of experience, she could not face them. Wheeling around, she hurried to Kozo. Tears threatened, but she held back the flow. She snatched the reins from where they dangled on the ground. The bay whinnied and flinched. Stealing one last glance at her uncle and the Ganoida bui, she stabbed her knife back into its sheath, grabbed a handful of black mane, and leapt astride Kozo.

She heeled her mount's flanks, urging him away from the critical stares behind her. Her heart hammered with the pounding of the animal's hooves against the snow-pack. On she raced, toward the hot springs. She pushed Kozo harder as he fought for ground up the side of a rise.

From behind a clump of brush and boulders, a jackrabbit jumped out, startling the horse. The bay pitched up, tossing his head.

The horsehair reins sliced through Winter Magic's grasp. Her palms burned. Snagging a tighter hold, she yanked hard on the lead. She fought for control, but the uneven ground and depth of the snow were too great for her.

Kozo reared again. He stumbled backward.

Without a saddle, Winter Magic had nothing but mane to grasp. Pitched from his back, she fell hard into the white powder. Air slammed from her lungs. She could not breathe. Eyes wide, she gulped. A pitiful wheeze sliced through her chest. Panic gripped her. No. She had to relax. Concentrating, she closed her eyes. Let go . . . be calm with yourself, the mind-chant grew louder in her thoughts.

Gradually she felt the pain in her chest ease. Cool air rushed in to soothe her fiery throat. She could breathe again, but it was not enough to comfort her. She saw her uncle's face again—saw the Ganoida bui and the men of her people. Her heart constricted and her shame returned. With another threat of tears, she swallowed.

Did Nighthawk speak the truth? Had she begun to see with only prejudiced eyes? Had she started to think of all white men as they did Indians? How could she help her people if she could not help herself? She needed to think this through—talk to someone. One person came to mind. The endearing face of Moon Dove, the white medicine woman who cared for her mother's people, the Maidu, formed in her head.

Again, you disobey! her inner voice tormented her. Tunupiuts sent you to pray.

She hesitated. Her uncle would be angry. He would not approve—had *never* approved of her visits with Moon Dove. She looked up, half expecting him to be standing in front of her. No one—only snowdrifts, sage, and icicle-draped pines. The wind whispered to her. *Muha ihovi.* Moon Dove had always listened to her problems and helped her in the past. With her gentle understanding she had all but replaced Winter Magic's mother.

Sniffling, she squared her shoulders. Winter Magic had to talk to her—even at the risk of traveling so far. She glanced up at the sun slipping from its zenith. If she started now, she might be able to get there by midnight. Yes. She would go to Moon Dove. *She* would know what to do.

Riding into the town of Daobeumawa'—Reno as the whites called it—always made Winter Magic uneasy. There were so many people, many more than those of her tribe left behind on the reservation Coo-yu-ee Pah near the big lake. Even at such a late hour the town was alive—with mostly men—with lots of drinking by both white and Indian alike, some never sobering at all.

How strange they all were. Their only thoughts were of money and how to get more—even when their pockets were running over with silver. They had lodging in one place and special dwellings for eating in another. She shook her head. The white world was a very restless and confusing place.

A drunken Indian woman staggered off one of the wooden walkways, nearly colliding with Kozo. "Damn horse," she said wickedly before her bleary-eyed gaze lifted.

Winter Magic grimaced with shame. No self-respecting Indian woman would ever use such language or find herself in such miserable condition. She could smell the rancid odor of whiskey. Liquor. Another foulness of the white man. One that turned a kind and gentle person into a demon. Her scowl deepened. She would help bring her people into the white world—she had to if they were to survive—but she wanted no part of their weaknesses.

Pulling her collar up closer to her ears, she shrank down into her coat and urged Kozo through town as quickly as she could without drawing attention to herself. A woman alone at night—Indian or white—was asking for trouble.

When she came to the big river Daoagawaka, running along the south side of town, she slowed the bay. She loved to watch the rapid flow of the Truckee. The water tumbled and churned, hurrying over the smooth stones as if it were trying to get somewhere very fast. She wondered what it might be like to be going someplace far away. But *she* could not. She still had much to do to help her family.

Sidling Kozo up to a small brick house at the edge of town, Winter Magic halted the bay, and slid down from her seat. She glanced up at the swaying sign hinged to the lip of the roof. GARRET J. SAMUELS, M.D. She looked at the house. Inside, all appeared dark and quiet.

She took Kozo's reins and led him around to the back. As she knew she would, she had come too late to speak with Muha Ihoui tonight. She would not wake the woman at this hour.

And, like Nighthawk, Dr. Samuels did not approve of the meetings between Winter Magic and his wife. Though he had never stopped Moon Dove from attending the Maidu and other Indians, Winter Magic knew that the white doctor would rather his wife stay completely away from them.

The doctor had not always felt this way though. Winter Magic believed that the pain of Moon Dove's abduction by the Bannock four years ago was still too fresh in his mind. It had turned his blood hot toward all Indians.

When Moon Dove had escaped the Bannock, he had been grateful that the Maidu had found and returned her to him—but that was all. He sent medicine every now and then and allowed his wife to care for them, but that did not mean he had to like it. And like it he did not. Neither did his white patients, especially his good friends the Taggerts.

Winter Magic tied Kozo to the fence surrounding the backyard.

He snorted loudly and shook his head.

"Shh, boy. You want to wake them?" she murmured. She patted his neck, then quietly crossed the open space to the porch. She would wait outside for morning to come before she would talk to Moon Dove. But no sooner had she curled up on the hanging bench-swing and pulled her coat tighter around her body than a nearby door creaked open.

"Komeni Tu'madai?" Moon Dove's throaty whisper scratched at the silence.

"*Pisha'*," she said with a nod, then held her hand out to her friend. Though the white woman was ten seasons older than Winter Magic, the shadows of night did little to age her youthful appearance. Straightening her robe, Moon Dove lifted a thick handful of corn-colored hair from the collar. She smiled. "I thought that was you."

"Did I wake you?"

"English, please." The slender woman moved to the swing. "You know how bad my Paiute is."

"Did I wake you?" Winter Magic asked, this time so that her friend could understand. "I tried to be silent. I did not wish to wake the doctor."

Moon Dove shook her head. "You didn't. Garret can sleep through anything—besides, he's gone." Waving her hand, she motioned for the younger woman to lower her feet to the porch. "What's wrong?" she asked after taking a seat beside her friend.

Feeling suddenly foolish for coming, Winter Magic could only shrug. She had recounted the event with the Ganoida bui and her uncle over and over in her mind as she rode into town. And each time her anger had lessened, leaving her even more confused and frustrated with her own emotions. After twenty-two seasons, why could she still not work out personal problems by herself?

"Komeni Tu'madai?" Moon Dove took her hand. "Has something happened? Have the Taggerts caused more trouble? Has someone been hurt?"

"*Kai*—no," she answered softly. "No one has been harmed."

Frowning, the white woman leaned nearer, her soft blue eyes appearing like silver coins in the moonlight. "Surely you haven't come at this late hour just to visit?"

"I need to talk."

A restless moment teased the silence.

"Let's go inside where it's warm."

"*Kai*. The doctor." Winter Magic darted a nervous glance toward the house. She remembered the last time he had come home and found her sitting inside with his wife. He had looked at her like the men from the Triple-T. It had frightened her.

"Wait here." Moon Dove squeezed her hand, then stood. "I'll be right back." Like a pale spirit, the woman seemed to float across the porch.

Winter Magic watched her friend disappear inside the house. Had she done right by coming here? Maybe she should have gone and prayed as her uncle had ordered. Yet how could she cleanse herself of a wrongdoing if she was not completely convinced she had committed one?

The door squeaked again, drawing her attention back to her friend. Two blankets draped one of the woman's shoulders.

The strong aroma of hot coffee filled Winter Magic's nostrils. She forced a smile to her lips. The smell was most tempting, but the taste—she cringed inwardly. Even with sugar added, she had never enjoyed the bitter flavor.

Taking her seat, Moon Dove held out a coverlet, then a mug. "It's been on the stove all night for Garret, but it'll have to do."

Winter Magic took the blanket and cloaked herself, snuggling deep into the folds. Sipping the black liquid, its heat bit her tongue as much as its sharp taste. She flinched, but managed to smile. "It is good."

Moon Dove sampled hers. The corners of her eyes crinkled. "It is a bit strong, isn't it?"

"*Kai*," Winter Magic lied. She did not want to offend her friend. "It is very good."

Raising her brows, Moon Dove took another drink. Back straight, she lifted her gaze to the night sky and sighed. "Just look at all those bright stars sparkling up there. Heaven's own glory twinkles in their lights."

Winter Magic followed the woman's line of vision. Moon Dove had a way of allowing a person time to gather her thoughts and speak when she was ready. She obviously knew Winter Magic was troubled, but did not push her into talking—an ability she herself had never possessed, but admired greatly.

"I have opposed Tunupiuts to come here tonight," she finally blurted out. She watched Moon Dove's face for a sign of disapproval. When it did not appear, she swallowed with relief, then continued. "Do you believe I see with prejudiced eyes?"

Moon Dove pulled a face. "What?"

"Tunupiuts believes this to be true."

"Did he tell you this?"

"*Kai.*" A shiver of apprehension wiggled up Winter Magic's spine. She was not quite certain she could rally her friend to her defense. "But it is what he believes."

"And do you think he's right?" Moon Dove held her posture taut, her tone challenging.

Sinking deeper into the blanket's warmth, Winter Magic refocused her thoughts. She had to find a way to win her friend to her side. "A stranger has come to our valley."

The blond woman's probing gaze leveled on Winter Magic. Still she did not speak.

"I saved him from an attack by the Pogonip."

"Pogonip?"

"The spotted mustang I told you about—the one my family needs to breed strong blood into our stock."

Cupping her hands around her mug, the woman nodded.

"He told me—the white man—he was a Taggert." Winter Magic stared into her coffee. "I was angered by this. There was a struggle."

Moon Dove's brows drew together, her expression becoming serious. "Did he hurt you?"

"*Kai*. He tore my shirt. Nothing more." She pulled her coat aside to display the shredded garment.

Moon Dove's eyes widened at the sight of the ripped piece of clothing. "Are you sure you're not hurt?"

Winter Magic nodded. "Tunupiuts and the other men from our ranch rode up before he could injure me."

"That's good." Her friend appeared to relax.

"I have never seen this Taggert before, yet Tunupiuts claims him to be a friend."

"Really? Does this friend have a first name?"

"He is called Lance."

"Lance has come home?" The white woman sounded startled.

"You know him, too?"

"No." Moon Dove took a deep drink, then pulled the blanket closer around her. "Shea told me about him."

"Ah." Winter Magic tested the heat of her own drink. Of all the Taggerts, Shea was the one and only that she could find tolerable. Many times in the past he had opposed his older brother and sided with her people over his own. Still, she could not understand his staying on at the Triple-T when he clearly protested his brother's hatred for her family and their attempt at ranching.

"The Ganoida bui has been away for many years, *pisha'*?"

"What does that mean—Ganoida bui?"

"Good—" She was unsure how to translate the

word into English. She pointed to her friend. "Good. Um—good in the face."

"Pretty?"

"*Pisha'*. Pretty."

"You mean handsome. For a man it's handsome."

"Ah. That is it. Handsome Eye."

Moon Dove chuckled softly. "Aren't both of his eyes handsome?"

"I do not know. He covers one with a black patch."

"Shea's never mentioned that his brother was injured. The man's been gone for such a long time, though. I suppose Shea may not know."

Winter Magic shrugged. "It must be so. Tunupiuts did not know of the covering before now, and he has been friends with the man since his boyhood."

Moon Dove nodded. "I see." Apparently waiting for Winter Magic to continue, she rolled her mug back and forth between her palms.

"It angered me that Tunupiuts did not punish this Lance for the way he dishonored me."

Like the fearsome mask of the Bear Dance, Moon Dove's features hardened. She stared at Winter Magic questioningly. "I thought you said he didn't hurt you."

"He did not—"

"I don't understand, then. How did he dishonor you?"

Winter Magic bit the soft flesh inside her cheek. She replayed the scene in her mind.

Leaning forward, Moon Dove raised her brows.

"He yanked me down from my horse," she

answered a bit too quickly. "He tore my shirt open and held me down."

"What provoked him to do this?"

Winter Magic glared up at the woman. She sounded like Nighthawk. She had not as yet heard the entire story, and already she acted as if it were Winter Magic's fault.

Hesitating a moment, Moon Dove tipped her head. "You're a very dear person, but I've seen you get angry before. You don't always give the other party a chance to understand what's happened."

Winter Magic stared at her friend. She had always held the greatest respect for the woman. She loved her. How could she not? Moon Dove had always helped her. Even when Winter Magic did not want to hear it, had not the woman always told her the truth?

She blinked. She *had* attacked the Ganoida bui first. He really had done nothing but protect himself. She had not explained her anger to him. How else was he to act? Feeling suddenly frustrated, she frowned. "Tunupiuts was right. I have sinned. The Ganoida bui did nothing wrong. I attacked him because he was a Taggert. My eyes *are* slanted against whites."

"*I'm* white."

Winter Magic ignored her friend's comment. She had never thought of Moon Dove as white. She shuddered. When she remembered how she had exposed herself in front of him, her eyes filled with shameful tears. "Muha ihovi, what he must think of Paiute women." Embarrassed, she allowed her head to droop.

"I'm sure once you and your uncle explain everything to the man, he'll understand."

"*Kai*, Muha ihovi. He will not."

After a moment her friend reached out and touched her hand. "Is there more? Something you haven't told me yet?"

Winter Magic's head dipped lower. She kept her eyes cast downward. She could not look at Moon Dove. Tears scalded her eyes. "I thought the Ganoida bui sought to humiliate me in front of my uncle and the other men. He looked at me so—so—" She could not find the words within her.

"Like he desired you?"

With trembling lips she nodded. "*Pisha*'. I suppose it could be so." She shook her head. "I am not sure."

"Look at me." Moon Dove took both mugs and set them on the porch, then clasped the younger woman's hands within her own.

Slowly Winter Magic lifted her gaze. Trying to see past the watery cloud, she squeezed her eyelids, but the spilled tears were quickly replaced by more.

"It's not always such a bad thing when a man looks at you like that, you know. Not all men are bad."

Winter Magic sniffled. She realized now that the Ganoida bui's gaze had not been anything like that of the other white men. "What *he* did does not make me cry. It is what *I* did that fills me with shame."

The older woman crooked a brow.

"I . . ." Winter Magic could not quite meet the soft blue gaze of her friend. She started to speak again, but her pride held her to silence. How could she have done such a disgraceful act?

"It's all right," Moon Dove crooned softly. She reached up and swept a long wisp of black hair from the younger woman's damp lashes. "There's no need to continue, Tu'madai."

The sound of her name being used so familiarly and tenderly sent a flood of warmth coursing through Winter Magic. Even though she was certain she had teased Moon Dove's curiosity, she was positive the older woman would not pry further. Never more than now, when she knew she was wrong, did she feel the maternal love and guidance from Moon Dove, that love and guidance her mother's death had left her without.

Her stomach fluttered, then settled. She did not need to go and pray for her sin. She had confessed to Moon Dove and had recognized the wrong she had done for herself. Was that not enough? Taking a cleansing breath, she lifted her gaze.

"Feel better?"

"*Pisha'*." Winter Magic nodded, then just as quickly shook her head. No. Talking to her friend would not set things right. She knew what she had to do. She had come here simply to justify her own actions against the Ganoida bui. But there was no defending her behavior. She had shamed herself as well as her people.

She stood up. "*Kai*, Muha ihovi. I must do as my uncle commanded. I must go and pray to purify my spirit."

A slow smile grew across Moon Dove's lips, and she held out her arms.

Chuckling to herself, Winter Magic hugged her friend. As always, and it seemed with very little effort, Moon Dove had shown the younger woman the truth of her own heart. Squeezing her friend's shoulders, Winter Magic squinted against the morning glare.

While they had talked, the sky overhead had lightened to a brilliant gray. But beyond, to the west, where her attention now moved, night had not quite given up to the dawn.

She pulled away from Moon Dove's embrace and stared out across the desert. And you, Ganoida bui . . . what must I do to purge myself with you?

◥3◣

At the first glimpse of smoke billowing dark above the Triple-T ranch house, Lance's heart picked up its pace. To a stranger the eerie shadows of the blue-gray dawn, mingled with the somber wail of the wind ruffling the alkaline surface of Honey Lake, might have been dissuading. But not to Lance. He was home.

He halted his mount just outside the gate. Through the frozen fog he saw someone move across the yard. Lantern light cast a circle of yellow-white around the man trudging toward the barn. Eldon. Hell struck a disarming blow to Lance's insides. He had hoped he would be greeted by someone else—anyone else—but not his older brother.

His eyes followed the man until the dark form melted into the frost-covered shades of the barn. Another light flickered, and Lance looked back at the house. Pale orange glimmered a welcome through the windows. Good. Shea must be up.

Lance tapped the rented horse's flanks, guiding him quietly toward the two-story dwelling. Masculine coughs and groans, morning sounds of the rousing hands, escaped a small slant-roofed building to his left. From various pens around him the waking animals added their voices to his welcome, with a mingling of clucks, moos, and neighs.

After halting at the single-post hitch in front of the house, he swung down and looped the reins around its iron horse-head. He started for the door but stopped midstep, one foot on the porch. The sound of a whip being cracked inside the barn lashed out at him. He snatched a resentful glimpse over his shoulder.

An animal brayed fitfully.

"Jedidiah?" Lance mumbled under his breath. "It can't be." He remembered the black mule his father had always used to haul supplies. The beast had been old then. After all this time he surely could not still be alive.

Another snap split the silence.

"Ah, hell!" Lance wheeled around and headed for the barn.

Another noise, even less inviting than the crack of the whip, grappled for his attention. Unmistakable, a rifle's breech-leaver cocked behind him.

"Hold it right there, mister."

Lance pulled up short. Instinctively he raised his arms. His gun flashed in his mind. He started to lower his right hand.

"I wouldn't if I were you."

Lance froze. He thought he recognized the voice, but not quite. "Shea?"

A moment of hesitation.

"Lance?" The robust timber softened to a youthful pitch. "Is that you?"

Smiling, Lance turned to confront his brother's familiar drawl. "Looks that way." He stretched out his arms.

Peeping over the distant mountains, daybreak fully exposed the boy now grown. Tall and lean, his rugged but rumpled appearance had that woke-up-in-a-hurry look. With a sudden gust of wind Shea's shoulder-length hair whipped across his unshaven jaw in streaks of blond and brown. Hazel eyes lit with excitement as he raced toward Lance. Shea slammed into him with a fierce hug.

Not having been around Shea as he developed, Lance was shocked when he felt the strength of his little brother's hold. He nearly knocked him off of his feet.

"Damn." Lance held the younger man at arm's length and looked at him. "You've been doing some growing while I've been gone."

Shea's suntanned face split into a wide grin. "Yup. I guess I have."

Another peal of leather lashed out from within the interior of the barn. Wood groaned, followed by a second bout of tormented neighs.

Lance scowled toward the unpainted side of the stables. "Is that old Jed taking that whipping?" But before Shea could answer, another crack disturbed the morning stillness. Enraged, Lance reacted. Spinning on his heels, he headed in the direction of the commotion, Shea a half-step behind.

"What the hell's wrong with El? Didn't he learn anything watching Pa with that animal?" Snow crunched loudly beneath Lance's boots as his long strides ate up the space between the house and the stable. He stepped through the entrance of the wide double doors just in time to see his older brother lift his arm for another strike at the scarred shoulders of a white-faced mule.

A movement on the ground caught his eye—the split ends of a bullwhip. Shifting his step, Lance planted one foot atop the braided strap.

Eldon yanked on the handle. His arm snapped midswing. The force of his movement slung him back a pace. "What the—" He jerked his attention around. Like just-struck flint, smoky-gray eyes met Lance's challenge. A scowl etching his face, Eldon tipped his head to one side and squinted. A slow mark of realization slid across his features.

In that instant Lance thought he saw a smile lift the corners of the man's mouth, but it vanished so quickly, he could not be certain. "Hello, El."

Eldon withdrew from his straddle-legged position, but kept his posture rigid. He singed Lance with a brusque once-over.

"It's Lance, El," Shea offered up from behind. "He's come home just like that doc back East wrote us he would."

"I can see that." Eldon seemed to be examining Lance's eye patch. After another moment his gaze fell on the trapped end of the whip. "You mind?"

Lance stepped off the leather as casually as if he had not known to what his brother referred. He strode past the man to the quivering mule still

staring walleyed behind him. Taking one strap of
the harness, Lance pulled the animal's head around
to face him. "This isn't old Jed."

"Nah." Moving closer to Lance, Shea pulled his
sheepskin jacket snugly around his naked torso and
fastened the buttons. "This's Willful. Old Jed died a
few years back. But he managed to sire this one
before he gave out."

"Willful, huh?" Lance lifted an amused brow and
patted the mule on his white forehead. If this
animal was anything like Jed, the name fit.

"So." Eldon began coiling the bullwhip, his eyes
remaining fixed on the task. "You've come home to
lick your wounds, hmm?"

Lance stiffened.

"El." Shea frowned at his oldest brother.

Pulling his coat aside, Eldon draped the rawhide
over the butt of his Colt. He obviously was not
pleased to see Lance.

Damn. He had not even said hello. Without
acknowledging his older brother's harsh words,
Lance brushed past Shea as he crossed the barn to
the tackroom. Entering the small cubicle, he caught
sight of a chestnut yearling darting past the window. He leaned across the workbench to watch for
a moment.

Head high, tail and mane flying, it exhibited its
magnificent prowess with a burst of speed around
the huge corral. Then just as quickly wheeled to a
stop and eyeballed the other horses as if to say,
"Hey, look at me."

Lance chuckled. He had missed the mornings
here watching the frisky play of the colts in the

early hours of daylight. How he wished he could feel that young and full of life again. He shook his head. A flood of self-loathing filled his being. Never more than here had he felt such utter worthlessness. What use was an ex-government agent with half his vision? Nothing.

"You okay in there?" Shea called out.

"Yeah," he hollered out. But it was a lie. He was far from *okay*. Lance located a tin of salve and a pile of clean rags on the shelf above his head.

Without further delay he gathered the implements and reentered the cavernous barn. He found the two men deep in conversation. He could not hear what they were talking about, but Shea looked mad, and Eldon, as Lance had always remembered him, appeared undisturbed. The discussion ended abruptly with Lance's intrusion.

Returning to the mule's side, he opened the can and dabbed the cloth into the ointment, then gently applied the balm. With the first touch the animal's withers skittered. He stamped one big forefoot and snorted a white puff of air.

"Whoa, there," Lance murmured, his own breath vaporizing in a thin cloud.

"You figurin' to start right in where you left off ten years ago, are you?" The venom of Eldon's words could only be matched by the hard line of his mouth, cinched tighter than a belly strap on a bloated horse.

"El—"

"It's okay, Shea." Lance had to work hard at hiding his disappointment. Even though he knew there was only a slim chance, he had hoped he would return home and find it a sanctuary to relieve his torment. But of course, that was not to be the case. He felt sure El did not really mean to sound so callous—it was just part of what made him Eldon Taggert. Still—

"Yeah, Shea. It's okay. Just look at him." Eldon gestured with an uplifted hand. "After all he's been through, workin' for that fancy governor's office in California, he can handle anythin'."

Lance ignored the remark. Things *had* changed since he had been gone. Eldon *was* callous. Lance concentrated on the mule's wounds. Quiet, so thick you could hear it, raced in and around the building.

"Hungry, Lance?" Changing the subject, Shea shifted his stance uncomfortably.

"Yeah, a little."

"Well, then. How's about continuing this treatment later and all of us going inside for a welcome breakfast. What'd you—"

"Speakin' of breakfast, what're you doin' here so early, anyhow?" Eldon broke in. "The doctor's wire said you'd be arrivin' on the six A.M. stage, December tenth. By my calculations that's today, ain't it?"

Out of the corner of his eye Lance saw Shea bob his head as if he was supposed to answer. "Bad weather kept holding us up at almost every stop. When we got to Cheyenne, I took the train the rest of the way. I wouldn't be here for another week if I hadn't."

"You rent a buckboard at the livery in Reno?"

Lance threw a half grin over the mule's shoulder. So his brother *did* care. "Is that what you were doing out here—hooking up the wagon to come into town after me?"

Eldon shrugged. He grabbed a pitchfork leaning against one wall and poked repeatedly at a clean pile of hay. He did not do anything with it—just probed around in the coarse stems. He reminded Lance of a child toying with a mound of tasteless greens on his supper plate. "Had to go in for supplies anyhow. Figured on savin' you a dollar or two's fee. But you're here now, so I guess that don't count for much."

"I appreciate the effort. Maybe I can take you up on it later, though."

"Later?"

"Yeah. The livery owner didn't have any more rigs by the time the train pulled in, so I left my bags with the station master and rented a horse instead."

"When the hell did you get in?" Eldon fixed a questioning bead on him.

"Yesterday morning. About nine."

"You get lost or somethin'? It don't take twenty-four hours to ride in from town?"

"No." Lance raised his brows.

Shea moved closer. "Well, where *have* you been, Lance? Did you have some trouble?"

Visions of the Indian girl standing so defiantly rigid holding her knife and glaring at him materialized in Lance's thoughts. He bit the inside of his jaw to keep from smiling. There was no doubt in his mind that she had wanted to see him killed—or maybe just tortured a little. But trouble? "No. I met up with Tunupiuts and a band of his men. We spent the night smoking and swapping stories about old—"

"Tunupiuts?" The corners of Eldon's mouth curled downward in a sneer. "Where?"

"A couple of miles above Long Valley Creek. Why?" Lance's curiosity was piqued. Eldon had never liked the Paiutes, or any other Indians—that was no secret—but he had always tolerated their presence.

"Dammit! I thought that bastard woulda learned his lesson by now."

"What're you talking about?"

"Tunupiuts was given permission by President Grant to start his own ranch, roundin' up mustangs." Shea rubbed his hands back and forth, then blew into them. "They settled up near Smoke Creek."

"Yeah, he told me." When Lance met his younger brother's gaze, he saw a look of despair—and warning.

"Did he also tell you that after snaggin' them broncs, he breaks them and sells them to the army?" Eldon railed.

"Great. I'm glad to see that they're finally doing for themselves again."

"Oh, yeah, they're doin', all right. They're tryin' to *do* us right out of twenty years of hard work. We can't sell the quality horseflesh we raise on this ranch for the undercuttin' prices they sell them brush-tailed nags for around here."

"I can't believe that they can outfit the entire United States Army with their horses, El." Lance tried to hold back the sarcasm in his voice, but there was no help for it. Eldon was just being pigheaded.

The Triple-T was well known throughout Nevada and California for its excellent breeding of quarter horses. "That's what this country's all about. A good healthy competition makes for a stronger economy."

"Economy hell!" Eldon's face reddened. "I don't give a tinker's damn about the country's economy. I'm talkin' about hangin' on to this ranch."

Lance tossed Shea a sidelong glance. No help there.

Shea stood staring at Eldon, his expression void.

Lance let his gaze drift around the interior of the barn. Plenty of clean straw and feed. Except for Willful, the animals appeared to be well attended, although he had noticed that there were not as many colts out in the pens with the mares as there should be. "The ranch doesn't look any worse for the wear." Gesturing to his brother's muscular physiques, he tried to lighten the mood with humor. "And it doesn't look like either of you have been going without meals."

Shea groaned.

"You tryin' to be funny?" Eldon glowered at him like a badger with his backside butted up against a stone wall.

"Oh, come on, El." Lance could not help but chuckle. "This valley's big enough to support two horse ranches. Tunupiuts can't beat the quality of our stock."

"*Our* stock? You've been here only a few minutes, and you're already tryin' to run things."

"I'm not—"

"Well, don't!"

"El, don't you think you're bein' a bit hard on Lance? Maybe he can help."

"We don't need his help. Did he come back to help when Pa died? Hell, no. I don't want him pokin' his nose in things now that don't concern him."

"If it concerns this ranch, it concerns me. This is still my home, too."

"Home." Eldon snorted. He thrust the tool back into the haystack, then leaned on the handle. "What the hell'd you really come back for, Lance?"

"El." Shea darted a nervous glance from one to the other.

Looking at his younger brother, Lance could not tell if his face had turned ruddy from the cold or embarrassment.

"You read what the doctor said," Shea continued. "He's just had that surgery on his—" He faltered, turning an even brighter red. "He needs some recuperation time at home."

Eldon moved around to a rail in front of the mule. Leaning back against it, he folded his arms over his chest and cocked his head to one side, studying Lance again. His examination started with the black patch, then wandered slowly downward and back up again.

Lance's hair prickled. He felt like a swaybacked nag at a stud sale. His body went taut. He did not like his brother's expression—one that appeared to be gauging the remainder of his worth.

"Is that the real reason? To recuperate?" Eldon finally asked. His face gave no hint to the preceding attack. "Or is it because you're scared? You're afraid the loss of that eye makes you less a man now, and you don't have anywhere else to go?"

Knuckles white, Lance's fingers gripped the can of salve. So here it was. The confrontation he had hoped to avoid with Eldon—or was it with himself? He stared at the man, considering him with more than a little reproach—or was it denial? Why had he come home? The governor had offered him back his job. But he had turned it down. How the hell did anyone expect him to continue doing his job with only one eye? Eldon had hit the nail on the head. Lance was not the same man as he had been before the accident—but hearing it only drew attention to his pain.

Frustration pumping through his body with every heartbeat, he pulled away his gaze. A single abrasion on the mule became his focus. "I was really hoping you wouldn't have turned out to be quite as cruel as Pa."

"What? You mean 'cause I ain't offerin' a lather of softsoap and perfumed words to greet you?"

"No, El," Lance answered dryly. Hands still atop the mule's back, he slouched his head down between his arms and breathed a heavy sigh. Eldon still had the same old gruff exterior, but he had grown colder, harder. He would not back down from this. But Lance had to. He was not ready for it yet. He squinted down at his boots. Hay flecked the scuffed cowhide toes.

Agonizingly aware of his weak appearance, he groaned inwardly, then looked up. "I mean, with this animal."

Eldon stared hard at Lance for a long moment before the tension in his expression eased. He almost grinned, but shoved a finger at the mule instead. "Bullheaded son of a bitch broke the whiffletree on the wagon." He pointed to the wooden pivot bar that fastened the harness to the rig.

Lance glanced at the split joint. He shook his head. "It looks pretty bad, but it can probably be fixed to hold long enough for one more trip into town. We can buy a new one there."

Eldon quirked a brow, then turned and strode toward the barn doors. "Good." He waved a hand in a dismissing manner. "You know so much about it, *you* mend it."

Lance shook his head. As he remembered things in the past, it seemed he had always done a lot of head-shaking whenever El was around.

"He doesn't mean to be so gruff." Shea slapped Lance on the back and smiled. "I know he's really glad to see you."

"How can you tell?"

Shea shrugged. "I watched his face when he read the telegram that big city doc sent us about you. Took your being hurt real bad. He's carried that cable around with him in his pocket for a month." Shea stared after the path of Eldon's departure, eyeing the yawning barn doorway with a memory-ridden expression. "Read it over almost every day."

Training his sights to follow Shea's line of vision, Lance felt a queer tightness in his chest. He had been raised with Eldon, and knew his older brother had a true fondness for him, but never to what extent. Why did he have to sound so hard? Could he not see the suffering Lance was going through?

"You know, El," Shea offered in a lighter tone.

"He's like Pa that way. He cares. He just doesn't know how to show it."

Just like Pa. Lance shifted his thoughts to his father. He had been wired of the heart attack four years ago. The sender had not signed the message—just gave the information in the barest of details. At the time he had figured it to be one of the ranch hands who had cabled. But now that he thought about it, he knew it had probably been Eldon. "Did you bury him next to Mother?"

"Pa?"

Lance nodded.

"Yup. Up under Ol' Char," Shea said.

Lance pictured the two graves side by side under the lone black oak near the hot springs where they had buried his mother twenty years ago. He felt a painful stab of grief pierce his concentrated efforts of composure. He shook it off. He did not want to think about his father. That on top of El's hostility would be too much.

With an uneasy smile he turned and slapped the can of ointment into his brother's hand. "Put this back for me, will you, Shea?" His voice scratched like sandpaper.

"Sure."

He waited for Shea to disappear inside the tack-room before allowing himself another breath. He did not trust his actions. He had not felt anything when he received the news of his father's death—at least, that's what he had told himself then. Why did hearing about the man's burial now affect him so powerfully?

His eyes strained against the glare of the overcast

light pouring in through the doors, as if from where he stood he thought he could see across the lake to Ol' Char. He should never have stayed away so long. A whirlpool of emotions churned his blood. He loved his father, yet hated him for what he had caused Neme to do.

The ghost of his beautiful wife haunted his thoughts, but her image was not quite clear. "Neme," he murmured thickly.

"What?" Shea had returned to his side without him realizing it.

A thick lump lodged in his throat. "Nothing." He turned away from Shea's questioning stare. Lance had guessed his return home would cause him to think about his dead wife, but he had not expected to be so emotional. His Adam's apple bobbed hard. God, how he missed her.

Damn it. Everything was crashing in on him. He had to get his mind on something else. Tossing the rag over the rail of a nearby stall, Lance clenched his eyes shut, then just as quickly refocused his sights. He reached for the harness and started to unhitch Willful. "Let's get you back to your pen, boy."

"Here. I'll do that." Shea took the lead from Lance. "You go on to the house and wash up. Stumpy's probably got breakfast about ready."

"Stumpy?" Lance allowed the twinge of grief to slip back into the shadows of his mind. "That old varmint still kicking?"

"Harder than ever." Shea rubbed his backside and chuckled.

"He still nursemaiding this family?"

Shea's head moved up and down like a cork, a smirk teetering his mouth. "Reckon he always will. We talked about hiring a woman for washing and such, but the old coot wouldn't hear of it. Says he isn't ready to be put out to pasture yet."

"Does he still make flapjacks as heavy as an anvil?"

"Ooo." Shea grimaced. "You remember, huh?"

Lance patted his stomach. "How could I forget. I'm still walking around with one or two."

Laughing, Shea clucked at the mule, guiding him into the pen. "I wouldn't let Stumpy hear you makin' jokes about his cookin' like that if I were you."

"Well, then." Lance threw a bearhug around his brother's neck. "Let's get into the house and wolf down some of those lead hotcakes so's he won't guess on his own."

But before either of them had taken a step, a tremendous commotion set up outside in the yard, men hollering and horses whinnying. Hurrying toward the doors, the two brothers nearly collided with a winded Indian boy as he charged through the opening. Lance judged him to be about nine years old, maybe ten.

"Hold on there, Tuhu'." Shea grabbed the boy by the shoulders. "What's all the hoo-ha about out there?"

"Hurry—hurry!" The boy directed them outside between panting breaths.

Shea careened his head in the direction of the noise. Not waiting for more, he stormed past Lance and out into the yard.

The boy lurched after him, but Lance yanked him back. "What's going on?"

The savage scream of a stallion's challenge echoed behind the corral.

"It is the Pogonip." Large black eyes bore into Lance. "He has come back to steal more mares."

4

Lance raced out of the barn just in time to see his rented mare tear free from the hitching post. It dashed across the yard and jumped the split-rail fence of the corral.

He ran after her as far as the gate leading into the pasture. Slamming into the wood, he watched her leap, saddle and all, over the back enclosure.

She sprinted after the three other ranch horses that had answered the call of a small herd of mustangs.

"Dammit!"

Rifle shots shattered in the air. A dozen half-dressed men joined him, their sights leveled on a white stallion barely visible in the fog.

Lance turned his head and strained the vision of his one good eye. If it had not been for the black leopard spots of the Appaloosa, he might not have seen the animal pacing the outer perimeter of the pen. "I'll be go to hell," he said under his breath.

Bullets whizzed all around the stallion.

"Hold it! Don't kill him!" Shea shouted above the blasting.

"Like hell."

"El—no!" Shea grabbed the barrel of the rifle and threw it upward just as it exploded.

Eldon whirled around. The back of his hand cracked against Shea's jaw.

The younger man hit the ground with an eruption of snow.

Lance flinched.

"Don't!" Eldon warned with a jutted finger.

The single command halted Lance even before he moved.

The other men stopped to stare at the brothers.

Glaring down at Shea, Eldon recaptured the breech of his rifle and cocked the lever. After ejecting a fired case, he turned around, steadied his elbows on the railing, and took another bead on the horse.

"El." Shea leapt back to his feet, but remained where he stood.

The stallion whinnied at his band in apparent retreat. Then as if to mock the man, the very self-possessed Appaloosa flared his nostrils and snorted. He moved a little closer and lifted his head.

Lance held his breath. He had never witnessed such a defiant act from a horse. So proud, the animal made a spectacular sight. His gaze darted between man and beast.

Eldon squeezed the trigger. A bullet splintered

the top of a post a couple of inches from the stallion's head.

With a triumphant shrill the Appaloosa reared, pawed the air, then wheeled and galloped toward his mares.

Eldon slammed the lever of his rifle back again. He lifted it for another shot.

Lance lunged forward and snatched the Winchester from his brother's grasp. He met the full force of Eldon's angry expression with one of his own. "You lose, El. You had your chance and you missed." His features easing, he shook his head. "I don't know how, but you did." His gaze moved to follow the animal.

Charging after his band, the stallion lowered his head and nipped a dawdling mare on the rump. When all of his herd was a good distance off, he turned and made one final stand. He postured another challenge, danced in place, and blew an aggressive snort. Then, arching his neck and tail, he shook his mane, whirled around, and disappeared into the frozen mist.

"I ask ya now. Ain't that the damnedest thing ya ever seen?" A familiar voice scratched like sand blowing in a rusty can.

With the utterance, an age-old joy flooded Lance. He would know that scratchy sound anywhere. Grinning, he spun around. He tipped his head for a clearer view of his longtime mentor. "Stumpy." The man had been given the name after a wagon accident left him shy a few fingers. Lance reached out and gripped the only remains of one leathery hand, a palm and thumb. "You old sidewinder."

"Old?" Like crisscrossing streambeds, a lifetime of wrinkles channeled Lester Tucker's face. But he squinted out of black eyes still young and full of spark. The once charcoal beard, now shimmering salt and pepper, concealed any trace of a smile. "Who you calling old, boy?"

Lance scanned the various faces of the ranch hands with a mischievous look—none of whom he recognized, but all of whom were his age or younger. "I don't see anybody else here I'd call *old*." He cut his gaze back to the hook-nosed man. "So I guess it must be you."

All at once Stumpy's hairy face split, exposing a tumble of tobacco-stained teeth. "Damned if it ain't you, Lance. Only one cub in the territory got enough gall to call me *old*."

"Get your gear, boys," Eldon interrupted. "We're goin' out after that brushtail."

"El." Shea grabbed his oldest brother's arm as he stalked past. "What're you aimin' to do?"

Glaring down at the offensive hand, Eldon's jaw tightened. He lifted his stare. "This makes two mistakes you've made this mornin'."

Shea did not make a move.

Lance quirked a brow. Good. It was gratifying to see that Shea had grown up with backbone.

Eldon jerked his arm free. His eyes shifted to Lance, the rifle, and back again. "You mind?"

With a shrug Lance pursed his lips and lifted the weapon.

Peering at Lance as if he were again sizing him up, Eldon took the Winchester. Then, without another word, turned and followed after the other men.

Shea moved to go after him, but Lance stopped the younger man.

"What about those flapjacks you were telling me about?"

Shea's hard stare remained leveled on Eldon.

"Let it go. He's just mad that he missed."

"Yup. This time he missed." The icy words slid out between Shea's clenched teeth. "But he's aimin' to fix that."

Lance looked over his shoulder at his retreating brother, then back at the spot where he had last seen the stallion. "I don't see that as happening."

Shea cut him a fiery glare. "Yup, well. You've been gone a long time." That said, he took off toward the house.

Lance darted Stumpy a quizzical gaze.

The older man lifted his mangled hand to Lance. "You say something about flapjacks?"

Lance could not help but think there had to be something he could do for his brothers. He watched as Eldon and the twelve or so ranch hands rode out in the direction where the mustangs had disappeared.

"C'mon, boy," Stumpy said.

The front door of the house banged, drawing Lance's attention. With angry strides Shea moved toward the barn. In another minute he returned to the yard with gear and horse. After saddling the black, he thrust himself into the seat. He cast a brief look at Lance, then heeled his mount and headed off the ranch.

Lance shook his head. "Some homecoming," he said under his breath.

"Believe me. Those two've been going at each

other about that damn horse ever since it showed up a few months back." He stepped behind Lance and slapped him lightly on the shoulder. "They're grown men now. Best ya leave 'em that way. Let Eldon and Shea take care of things betwixt them themselves."

Lance considered Stumpy's words. Yeah. He would let them handle it. He had his own problems to work out. Eldon had been right. Lance was only here for a short time. All he wanted was a little rest and recuperation—nothing more.

Within an hour Lance had cleaned himself up and headed for the kitchen. He pulled out a chair and sat down at the table.

"Feel better now that ya had a wash-up?" Stumpy asked. Gripping a black skillet, he flipped one large hotcake onto a plate. He set the breakfast in front of Lance. "Took a shave whilst ya was at it, hmm?"

Lance rubbed the nakedness of his upper lip. He had worn the mustache for almost a year while he was on his last case. "Yeah. I needed a change."

Stumpy shook his head. "Men ain't s'pose to have a face like a baby's butt. How'er ya s'posing to keep that kisser a yers warm?"

"I'll manage."

"With Reno gals purty-near a full day's ride away, I'm doubting that one, boy."

Forking a chunk of flapjack, Lance looked up to see the same Indian boy he had spoken to earlier enter the kitchen with an armload of timber. He nodded, then took a bite.

The kid ignored him.

Lance tried again. He wiped his mouth on a red gingham napkin and smiled.

The boy appeared uninterested. Yet even as he moved, his gaze held Lance's.

"Ya got that whole stack a wood chopped, Tuhu'?" Stumpy asked the child.

He nodded, his dark eyes staring at Lance in silent fixation.

"Good boy." Stumpy patted the kid's dark head. "Best ya go and git after the rest of yer chores now before El gits back and thinks yer slackenin'."

After dumping the kindling in the bucket next to the stove, Tuhu' turned around. He did not move—hardly blinked.

Uncomfortable beneath the boy's steady scrutiny, Lance straightened. Would it never end? Why did people have to stare? A one-eyed animal got more respect. He had not changed. He was still a man. No. Only half.

"Tuhu'."

The kid glanced at Stumpy.

"Ya hear me, boy?"

Coal-black eyes acknowledged the man with only a blink.

Stumpy motioned toward the door. "Well, then. Git after it."

With a start the boy hurried out of the kitchen, his face as expressionless as when he had entered.

Coffeepot in hand, Stumpy moved up to the table. Without asking, he poured Lance another cup. "Good kid, that one."

Lance swallowed another bite. "Who is he?"

"His name's Tuhu'."

Lance smiled at the meaning of the boy's name. "Wildcat, hmm?"

"Yessir. An' ain't he jist that?" Stumpy chuckled. "He's one of them Maidu from up Secret Valley way."

"What's he doing here? El didn't seem to have become any softer toward the Indians. How come he lets him stay?"

Stumpy crossed back to the stove and retrieved another mug from the shelf beside it. He poured a portion of the strong liquid for himself, then shrugged.

This was not like the old grizzly. Stumpy knew everything that went on around the Triple-T.

Lifting the pot, the man raised his brows. "Ya want some more?"

"You just gave me some."

Stumpy simply nodded and returned the coffee to the stove. But after only one sip, the old guy tossed the remaining liquid of his own cup into the washtub.

Lance shot a curious look at the kitchen door, then back at his friend. "What's going on here?"

"What d'ya mean?"

"Oh, come on, Stumpy. You know what I mean." He gestured toward the door with a dip of his head. "What's up with the Indian kid?"

"Lance. Things ain't changed too awful much 'round here since you left. Some folks still gits mighty sore when a fella goes an' pokes his nose where he shouldn't oughta."

Puzzled, Lance frowned. He groped for answers like a blind man in a whorehouse. His past training as an investigator spurred his inquiry further. "Why? Somebody trying to hide something?"

The older man's posture stiffened. Turning slowly to face Lance, he glowered down. His left eye twitched slightly.

Surprised, Lance pulled back. That was it. Someone *was* trying to keep the boy a secret. But why? Something about the kid did appear to be familiar, yet Lance knew he had never seen him before today. A playful thought triggered in his mind. He remembered how his older brother had always chased after the Indian girls when the two of them had been younger. "Eldon?" He flashed Stumpy a spicy grin, but took it back just as quickly when his friend shoved a finger out at him.

"Ya jist hold on now."

"You trying to tell me that Tuhu' is Eldon's son?"

Stumpy dropped his rail-thin frame onto a chair across the table from Lance. "I ain't trying to tell you nothing."

"But that's it, isn't it?"

Like a hawk after prey, Stumpy stared at him another minute or two. He shook his head. "No chance of you jist letting this go, is there?"

Lance raised his brows. Setting his fork in his plate, he pushed it aside. "Is it that bad?"

"Not to my way of thinking, it ain't. But you know Eldon." He paused. "Nah. I guess ya don't."

With a half smirk, Lance cocked his head. "You're right about some things not changing around here, Stumpy." He squinted. "But El? How the hell did this happen? He's always hated Indians as much as Pa."

"Ye'r right there. But there was this one little

Injun gal that Eldon jist couldn't seem to leave alone.''

''Must've happened right after I left. The kid looks to be about ten or eleven.''

''Yessir, about that.'' Stumpy's head bounced up and down.

Remembering the terrible fight between him and his father when he had announced that he was going to marry Neme, Lance flinched. ''How'd this come out?''

''Who the hell knows? Don't make a piss-ant's mound worth a difference, no how.'' Stumpy rubbed his bristly jaw with his crippled hand. ''All's I know for certain's that yer pa found out. And that was enough.''

''Bet he was fit to be tied.''

''That's one helluva mean fact, that is.'' Stumpy leaned forward. ''Thought that man was going to rip every inch of flesh off that boy's back. Beat hell outa Eldon with that damn bullwhip a his.'' The older man's dark eyes took on a mournful look. ''No telling how far he would've gone if I hadn't drawn down on him with my rifle.''

Lance grimaced. It was hard to believe his own father could have done such a thing. ''You're saying Pa whipped him?''

Stumpy's head bobbed. ''Yessir. Whupped him worse than he ever beat that ol' mule a his. Said he'd be damned if he'd have two Injun-loving sons.''

Lance stiffened. He punished the napkin he held, twisting it around his fingers, as if it were his father's thick neck.

''Sorry, boy,'' Stumpy said after a long silence.

Lance tossed the linen onto the table with feigned nonchalance. He shoved the anger and pain of his father's words down with all the other past offenses the man had imposed on him—into the dark recesses of his mind where no one could see them. "So. How'd the boy end up here?"

Stumpy's mood changed. A grin plastered his face. "He jist waltzed in one day last summer and announced that his ma was dead and that he was looking for his pa." The entirety of the man's spindly body jiggled with a laugh. "That boy's a Taggert, all right. Got more spunk than good sense."

Knowing his friend did not mean his statement as an insult, Lance chuckled with him.

"Why, that young cub marched right up to Eldon and told him bright and clear as daylight who he was and that he was staying put."

Leaning back in his chair, Lance flicked a glimpse toward the door. He remembered the boy's undaunted expression. If nothing else, he could well believe that. "And Eldon just let him stay?"

"Not right off. Thought I was going to have to step in betwixt another son and his pa." Stumpy leaned closer still. "He knocked that boy down so hard I swear I heard the kid's teeth rattle."

Lance had never remembered El being brutal with either himself or Shea—or anyone else for that matter. But that was when they had been kids. It seemed the Eldon he had known had changed into a shadow of his father. "Then what happened?"

"Why, that stubborn little scutter got up. He looked Eldon straight in the eye and said nothing

short of being sent to the Great Spirit at the hands of
his own pa was going to make him leave."

"Really?" Lance snorted.

"Yessir." Stumpy squinted out of one eye.
"Kinda reminds me of another mule-headed pup
that use to scamper 'round these parts, don't it
you?"

Recalling the many times Lance had challenged
his own father, he flashed a sheepish smile. "Yeah,
I suppose so." More and more he wished he still
had some of that spunk Stumpy was talking about.

"More than one time, as I recall, I had to git
betwixt you and yer pa, remember?"

"Yeah." Lance raised his brows. "I do indeed. But
there were good times here, too. Pa and I didn't
always argue. Like when he gave me Patches for
my fourteenth birthday."

"That little pinto he brought back from one of his
Denver buying trips?"

Lance nodded.

"Yessir, I do recall. Handsome little beast it
were."

"God, but I loved that horse—and Pa for giving it
to me. It was like we were real friends again. Like
when I was just a kid—before Ma died." His throat
closed with the mention of his mother. He could
remember the way her arms felt when she hugged
him, but not her face.

Stumpy smacked his lips with a grimace. "Pure
angel from heaven that woman was. Yer pa was a
sight different when she was alive, that's a pure
fact." He gave Lance a careworn look. "At least she
managed to live out here in this desert long enough

for Shea to come wriggling out into the world a'fore she passed on.''

Lance's stomach squirmed with anguish. Damn it! He had not come back for all this. Did every little remembered pang have to settle in all at once? He should have gone to San Francisco like the doctor suggested. Rested. Had some fun. Why instead had he chosen to come back to the one place that would cause him to feel the discomfort of his physical torment even more?

But was it all terrible? his inner voice questioned him.

''Too bad yer pa killed that animal. It was a good little horse,'' Stumpy announced. ''Shea was jist too darn little to hang on was all.''

Lance blinked. He called to mind the fateful scene of his youth.

''I can do it myself,'' Shea had announced from atop Patches. He gripped the reins in one scrawny hand and clamped his legs as far around the animal's belly as he could reach, but the stirrups still dangled a good six inches below his feet.

''He's a little big for you, Shea. You let me lead him, okay?'' Lance took hold of the bridle. He started the pony off at a walk, but Shea was not happy with that.

''I wanna go faster.''

Clucking to the horse, Lance urged him to a trot, running alongside the animal.

''Faster—faster!'' Shea squealed.

''You watch out for him!'' his father had yelled from the other side of the corral.

''Okay, Pa.'' Lance waved.

''Look at me.'' Shea grinned proudly beneath a

hat two sizes too big. "I'm a real buckaroo." Just then Shea yanked hard on the reins, stripping them from Lance's grasp. He gouged the pony in the flanks before Lance could regain his hold. "Gitty-up, Patches."

The little horse squealed. He bolted across the field, straight for the fence.

"Hang on!" Lance whistled as loud as he could. He had been training the animal to return to him on that command. Even after two weeks of working with the horse, he still had not been able to teach Patches to acknowledge the summons. But in that single, awful moment the pony skidded to a stop.

Shea pitched into the railing.

Pretty as you please, that pinto wheeled around and trotted up to Lance.

Knocked unconscious, Shea lay motionless on the ground.

In the moments that followed, Lance could only think of his horse.

His father stalked from Shea to the little beast, pulled out his Colt, and fired.

"Hey! You okay, boy?" Stumpy asked.

Lance blinked, then swallowed. He thought the vividness of that memory had been long forgotten. He could not answer. He glanced up at Stumpy, the time-worn ache squeezing his throat closed. Was this what it was going to be like now that he had returned home? Damn. He thought he had buried all these nightmares when he laid Neme to rest and left the ranch.

The harder you run from your troubles, the harder they chase you. He remembered the old saying he had read somewhere a long time ago.

The room tilted, threatening to swallow him up. Stumpy's face wavered. Lance had to get some air. Lurching to his feet, he grabbed his Stetson from the wallpeg near the door.

"What's wrong? Where ya off to now?" Stumpy called after him.

"I want to go for a ride—see how much the ranch's changed."

"Ya jist got here. Damn, boy. Ya don't have to jump up and rush out in such an all-fired hurry, do you? You think the ranch's going to run off or something?"

Lance cut a brief look over his shoulder. He knew he had startled the old guy, but it could not be helped. The demons were closing in all around him. He had to get out for a while. He offered his friend a consoling smile. "I'm going to take one of the horses."

"Ya gonna be gone long?"

Lance shrugged. "As long as it takes." With that he slapped his hat on his head and opened the door.

"What's that suppose to mean?"

Stumpy's question barely penetrated Lance's consciousness as he closed the door behind him. He had to regroup—needed to think. He had not been prepared for all of this at once—or even separately. He had thought the years away from home had erased the painful memories. But no. They were all still here—waiting—hiding like a wolf in the trees.

He crossed to the barn with restless strides. After outfitting a dun from one of the stalls, he led it into the yard and stepped up into the stirrup.

The breeze picked up and he turned his face from the frigid bite of the wind. God. Everything hurts around here. He had to get away from it. With one last glower toward the family house, he flanked the horse to a start. And this time he just *might* go off to San Francisco.

5

An hour before sundown Winter Magic arrived at a fork where the hot springs of Tupi' twaba met that of a cool stream a few miles north of the Triple-T. She had no time to bathe—barely time to strip off her clothing and ask her prayers of repentance—before the glaring light of day gave up its powers to the night.

"Give me a dream, Great Spirit. Tell me what I must do. I have shamed my uncle as well as my people with the white man, the Ganoida bui." Knees tucked beneath her, shivering from the cold, Winter Magic held her arms bent, palms up in the direction of the waning star of day. Reflecting off the snow, the last gleam of twilight hurt her eyes, but she met its harshness with a steady gaze. "I do not make excuses for the sin of my doing. I ask forgiveness—to be shown the way to walk in the light of your smile once more."

Fingers to thumbs, she touched her forehead. She ended her prayer with a song of thanks for the answer she hoped the Great Spirit would give her.

Standing, she quickly hurried to the small fire she had made earlier. She rubbed her hands together over the flames. Steam rose up from the springs, beckoning her with its warmth. She moved toward its waiting comfort, but stopped. What about the little beings that were said to live in the hot springs, the water babies? They had never been known to hurt people, but— She shook her head and made for the water only to pause again at its edge. Only shamans and people with powers could see them. Was this not true? The icy air nipped at her skin. She was not certain and did not care to test the fact.

Rushing back to the foot of the huge mound of rocks she had chosen for her camp, she grabbed her coat and draped her shoulders. Tomorrow, in the morning, she would bathe. For tonight the fire would have to keep her warm.

She was so cold, she could scarcely make her fingers work the studs after slipping on her pants. Her feet stung from the frigid bite of the frozen ground, yet she remained impassive and without complaint. With chattering teeth and shaking hands, she bent over, hopping on one foot, then the other, as she pulled on her moccasins.

A sudden uneasiness gripped her.

Kozo whinnied.

Her stomach tightened. Something, or someone, watched, behind her. She whirled around, eyes wide.

Catching the firelight with an unholy glint, an eye

blinked at her from a silhouetted figure sitting atop the shadow of a horse.

Her breath caught. Was this the sign she had asked for, or had the Great Spirit sent a ghost to frighten her? Had she angered the god that much? Her heart raced within her breast. She *had* sinned. She must accept her punishment with courage if she was to be forgiven. She swallowed hard. "I am Komeni Tu'madai. I am the one you seek." Bowing her head, she waited for the decision of her fate.

"Winter Magic?"

Like a spark to flint, panic flared within her. She had not expected the spirit to sound so—so human.

The voice came at her again in her own tongue. "Is that you, Winter Magic?"

A lump formed in her throat. Squeezing her eyes closed, she tensed, then nodded.

Leather creaked, followed by the sound of horse's hooves crunching across the snow.

"Mind if I share your fire?" The rise and fall of the deep-set tones belonged to no spirit.

Her eyes snapped open. She squinted into the growing darkness. The image moved nearer. This was not a ghost—but a man—and he was white. But who was he? Her body stiffened. The Triple-T lay just across the lake. It must be one of the men from the Taggert Ranch.

Motionless, Winter Magic scarcely allowed herself to breathe. She was an Indian, a woman, and alone. Three things a man from the Triple-T would be delighted to discover. She darted a glance at her knife. It lay mere inches from her feet.

Still outside the glow of the fire, the man spoke

again. "What're you doing here? I thought Tunu-piuts sent you to the springs at Sharp Mountain."

Winter Magic cast the figure a questioning stare. Only one white man knew where she had been sent. The Ganoida bui. Her previous anger flashed, but she held her tongue. What was *he* doing here?

Entering the firelight, he came into view. Clean and smooth, his features loomed before her, spectral shadows dancing across a bold and beautiful face. Like the hoarfrost air seeping up from the ground, his one gray eye focused on her. He started to dismount, then fell back onto his saddle. His gaze dropped below her face, then darted to the fire. "I—uh . . . You got a new—uh—"

She looked down. Her eyes rounded. Her shirt—she had forgotten her shirt! Her face flamed with embarrassment. Her lips went dry, and she fought the urge to moisten them. How could this have happened again? She had committed the same sin twice. The Great Spirit would be even more angry with her. Humility gnashed at her rage.

Spinning around, her back to the man, she snatched up her blouse and gathered her knife with what she hoped was a concealed movement. "*Pisha'*. A friend, Moon Dove, gave me one of hers."

She struggled beneath her coat, tugging on the garment as quickly as she could. She tied the sheath of antelope skin containing her blade at her waist. With a keen ear she listened for the man's actions. His boot chomped the snow as he stepped down from his horse.

After fastening the last of her buttons, she turned back to face him. "Why are *you* here, Ganoida bui?"

she asked, yanking out her hair from within her jacket.

The man grinned. "After our—uh—meeting yesterday, I think we can move beyond the formalities. Why don't you call me Lance?"

"Lance," she repeated hesitantly. "Why are you—"

He shook his head. "I asked you first."

Reluctant to answer, Winter Magic remained silent. She did not know this man. And though her uncle trusted him, she did not. Still, what harm could it do? She kept her tone even. "I do not like the strong smell of the waters at Sharp Mountain. This place is better for prayers."

Fingering his reins, the Ganoida bui looked at her thoughtfully. "You still mad at me?"

How was she to answer him? She was unsure herself. Without losing her composed expression, she lifted her brows.

A slow smile turned his mouth heavenward.

She found herself watching the uplift of its curve. How was it she had not observed its subtle charm earlier?

He must have noticed her stare. His grin broadened and he rubbed his upper lip. "I—uh—" He paused, then switched to English. "Shaved."

Winter Magic frowned.

"You know." He lifted his nose with one finger and scraped at his face with his other hand. "Shave?"

He looked so funny, she nearly laughed.

"That's better." He appeared to relax. Leading his horse to where she had hobbled Kozo, he tied his mount to a branch of greasebrush, then returned to the fire. "You don't look quite so mean with a smile."

Winter Magic tensed.

"No—no." He looked down at the ground. He seemed to be searching for something. "Now, where'd it go?"

"You have lost something?"

"No—you did."

Puzzled, Winter Magic glanced downward. She could see nothing but their footprints in the snow. "You make a mistake. I have lost nothing." She looked up.

"So where's that smile you just had?"

Heat rushed to her cheeks. This was something Winter Magic had not expected. Indian men did not speak with women in such a bold and easy manner as this. Feeling a sudden rush of warmth, she fidgeted with a button on her coat. She averted her gaze to the leaping flames.

Squatting, he peeled off his gloves and held his hands up to the flames. "I was on my way back to the ranch when I saw your fire."

"Ah." She felt somewhat relieved, yet unexpectedly awkward with his presence. Maybe if she went about her business, he would go away. Kneeling, she took out her knife and began to stab at the snowpack. She would have to clear away a place for herself to sleep if she was to stay warm during the night.

"You don't mind if I stay a while and chase off some of the cold before I ride on, do you?"

What should she do now? It was unseemly to sit and talk with a man who was a stranger. Her head bent to her task, she stole a cautious glimpse at him.

She would offer him the comfort of her fire and nothing more. "*Kai*." Maybe he spoke the truth. Maybe once he had warmed himself, he would leave her to her prayers. Concentrating her efforts on her work, she returned her focus to the ground.

Silence yawned, passing the stretch of time it took her to remove a large enough section of ice for her to lie down. After completing this, she began to do the same with the marshy earth.

Observing her in stilted quiet, the man moved up on one of the smaller rocks, stretching out his legs so that his feet were nearest the fire.

She felt the weight of his gaze heavy upon her. Why did he stare at her so? The blade in her hand flashed in the fluttering light, its color reminding her of the man's steel-gray eye. Slowing her movements, she had the most compelling urge to turn and look at him again.

"What *are* you doing?"

She jumped at the sound of his voice. "I will sleep here."

"That much I figured out."

Covered in damp soil, Winter Magic's hands felt numb. Standing, she brushed off her knees and moved to the hot spring. The Ganoida bui asked strange questions. He looked like a man that had spent much time sleeping out under the stars. Had he never dug out a winter bed?

A movement tugged her attention.

He had come to crouch beside her.

She drew up tight.

"What's all that for?" He nodded toward the shallow pit she had just prepared. Warm as the water in which she dipped her hands, the Ganoida bui's voice trickled through her.

"I have told you. It is where I will sleep." She kept her eyes trained on the spot where the gurgling spring joined the cool waters of the stream. She did not trust herself to look at him. "I have only my pony blanket. I must spread a covering of embers on the ground and pull the earth over it."

His gaze remained fixed on the open spot. "And that keeps you warm all night?"

She nodded. "Very warm." Daringly, she peered up at him through a wisp of her black hair. "You have never done this?"

"No. But it sounds like it'd work." He looked back at her. "Mind if I try it?"

Pulling a frown, Winter Magic flashed him an open stare. Did he mean to stay here? With her? "Your ranch is not far. You do not wish to sleep in comfort?"

He looked sideways at her. His serious face glowed in the firelight. "I'm sorry. I wasn't thinking." He started to rise.

"Thinking?" Tucking her wet hands under her coat, she stood up beside him.

"Yeah. I'll be disturbing your prayers." He moved toward his horse. His light expression plummeted.

Something inside of her, something she herself was barely aware of, spurred her forward. She held up a hand. "*Kai.*"

Reins in his grip, he glanced back.

"You do not disturb me, Ganoida bui." She bit her tongue against the lie. She did not know why, but this man did more than just disturb her. He caused her to forget who she was and what she was supposed to be doing, to do things she would normally never do. Like invite him to stay the night. "You may camp here tonight."

He turned back to face her, his head cocked to one side, the sweep of his gaze taking in more about her than she wished him to know.

A rush of heat flooded Winter Magic's body. Why did she feel suddenly shy when he looked at her, yet at the same time tingle with delight?

"Thanks. I'd like that." He turned his back to her. "I'd really like a chance to get to know you."

Winter Magic's eyes widened. Whites were indeed bold. Studying his movements, she flicked a bold glance down the length of his muscular frame.

Tall and lean, his stalwart carriage boasted a man of strength and character.

Winter Magic's stare held steady. Despite the cold, her palms grew moist, her breathing quickened. I, too, would like the chance to know you, Lance Taggert.

He tethered his horse again, then removed the saddle and walked over to her. "That is, I'd like to if you'll show me how to fix my bed." A playful smile beckoned her attention.

She blinked. Caught watching him, Winter Magic was held to silence. What would he think of her? She was the niece of Nighthawk, tribal leader of the Paiute Nation. Was this the action of one that was supposed to be a respected member of their tribe? She must regain control of her emotions. She peered at him more intently. Maybe he *was* the sign she had asked the Great Spirit to give her. He certainly provoked strange thoughts within her. If so, she would not challenge her fate. She would try. She must offer him this small trust? She cleared her throat. *"Pisha'.* I will show you how."

Within a short time they had completed a place to sleep for each. For nearly half an hour they sat cross-legged, each on his own blanket, lost in thought.

Neither spoke, though in the moments that passed, Winter Magic glanced up on more than one occasion to find the man gazing at her. This she found most unsettling. "Why do you watch me, Ganoida bui?"

"I thought we decided it was Lance."

"Pisha'. I will try to remember. Why do you—"

He shrugged before she could repeat the question. "You remind me of someone I knew a long time ago."

"Your woman?"

He stared at her long and hard. "Are you always so blunt?"

She raised her brows. "It is wrong to ask?"

He smiled, his gaze taking on a faraway look. "No—just unexpected."

"Was she beautiful?"

"Mmm—very."

"And I remind you of her?" Winter Magic felt pleased that he might think of her as beautiful.

"In some ways."

"How?" Neither her curiosity nor her pride would back down. She wanted to hear him say it.

"Well . . . she was Indian like you."

Winter Magic's heart plummeted. Was that her only similarity? "That is all?"

Seemingly captured by the leaping flames of the campfire, he remained silent.

Intrigued, she watched the man. It was unusual for a white-eye to take an Indian for his woman in *this* valley. She pressed him for more answers. "Where is your woman now?"

If he had thrown a knife at her, he could not have pierced her heart deeper than he did with the haunted look he leveled on her. His gaze was filled with pain. "She's dead."

Her throat closed. She felt sorry for him. It was pitifully evident that he had loved his woman deeply. How could she have been so thoughtless? Would she ever learn to control her foolish pride? She could not hold his stare. The pain in his eyes was too great.

Feigning indifference, she looked away. Then, when she was sure he had diverted his attention, she returned her gaze to him.

She watched him stir the fire embers with a stick, and she felt a sudden stir within herself. She had indeed misjudged the heart of whites. Not all were cold and calculating, as she had believed—at least, this one was not. She smiled at herself. The Great Spirit was most wise. He had sent her the sign she had asked for. He had sent Lance Taggert to mark the path she was to follow. Puzzled, she frowned. Why him? Her curiosity plagued her again. What made him different?

She tipped her head and studied the man. She became aware of the size of his hands, the length of his fingers, and the subtle flex of his tendons as he gripped the piece of wood. Her heartbeat picked up a pace.

Allowing her gaze to roam over the white man at will, she realized that Lance Taggert was very pleasing to look upon. Her palms moistened and she smiled thoughtfully. Where is it that the Great Spirit would have you lead me, *Ganoida bui*?

Alarm shot through the core of her body. The way this man caused her to flood with warmth was both soothing and dangerous. She had only known this sensation with one other. A vision of Owl Eyes, the gentle-hearted infatuation of her youth, flashed in her memory. Had he not caused such a reaction within her on another night such as this? She swallowed hard. She had paid a dear price for what she had learned that night. And so had he. What would this night cost her?

She needed a distraction. Toying with a crystal stone she used for meditation, she pressed her fingers against a sharp edge. It did not cut, but the dull pain it inflicted was enough to draw her away from her wayward thoughts. She looked out and studied the density of the frozen cloud moving in around them.

"Looks like it's coming in thick."

The man's voice pulled Winter Magic from her musings. She stared at him for a minute.

"The mist." He gestured in the direction where she had been watching.

"Ah." She blinked with a nod. "*Pisha'*. It is most beautiful."

"Aren't you afraid of it? I thought most of your people feared they'd catch pneumonia in fog like this."

Shaking her head, Winter Magic smiled. "I am a child of the Komeni. Listen," she said, her voice softening to a whisper. "If you are very quiet, you can almost hear the ice-needles striking one another within the Pogonip."

The man darted a quizzical gaze out at their surroundings. "Wait. You mean he's back?"

"Who?"

"That stallion that nearly trampled me yesterday morning."

"*Kai.*" Winter Magic smiled. The Ganoida bui was confused. "He is not here. It is the fog."

With raised brows, the man shook his head. "I thought you said the Appaloosa's name was Pogonip."

"*Pisha'.* That is what my people call him. As I told you on our first meeting, this is *his* weather. He is the Pogonip puku'."

"The horse of white death. Hmm." The man picked up a broken tree limb and tossed it onto the fire. "That's appropriate."

"He is said to be guided by the spirits of *yambautom*, the freezing month." She lowered her voice, for it was not always safe to let the spirits hear humans speak of them. "He only comes out to raid when the *pogonip* appears."

"That explains his boldness at the ranch this morning."

"He stole more horses from the Triple-T?"

"Yeah. Got away with three mares, including the one I rented from the livery in Reno."

Winter Magic grimaced. "This is very bad. There will be more trouble."

The white man snorted. "I'll say. Thought Eldon was going to pop a blood vessel when he tried to shoot that animal and missed."

Raising up, she drew her legs underneath her, then sat on her heels. "Your brother tried to kill him?"

"Yeah."

Winter Magic stared in shocked disbelief. "Why does he do this? Why does he hate us so much?"

"Hey. Hold on there." The white man leaned closer. "He missed, okay? Your Pogonip's safe."

Slowly the words sank in and she relaxed a little. "Tell me, Lance. Why does your brother want to see us fail? We do not hurt him. We only wish to better ourselves—to live in peace. Is this such a bad thing?"

"I don't understand. If that horse's causing so much trouble, why would killing him cause your people so much frustration?" Brows furrowed, he peered at her with a puzzled expression. "I've never seen El act so crazy. What's going on around here anyway? If I didn't know better, I'd swear this valley was in the middle of a war."

Uncertainty rode a hard path within Winter Magic. She cocked her head. "A person *could* see things that way." She paused. How would the Ganoida bui take what she was about to tell him? "Your brother wishes to kill the stallion so we may not have the Pogonip."

"Why's that?" He sounded skeptical.

"We, too, have a ranch. It is there." She pointed toward the north. "Near Wahahu, what you call Smoke Creek. It was given to us by your President Grant. We call it Ta'nowani Asta' Tuhu'ya."

"Run of the Red Deer." He nodded. "Yeah. Shea told me."

"Ah. Then you know what we do?"

"No—not everything." He sighed heavily. From the forlorn expression on his face, he appeared as if he were not certain he wanted to know.

Winter Magic was not sure how to continue. What if, when she was finished telling him, he reacted like his older brother? Still, she felt compelled to explain the best way she could. "A few years ago we were left starving on the reservation of Coo-yu-ee Pah. It was the winter of my fifteenth year. Many of my people died—including a girl-child born to Tunupiuts and Yitakam." A single tear sprang up in Winter Magic's gaze. Her heart felt heavy with the remembrance of the baby's death. She glanced at the Ganoida bui.

Sitting very still, appearing to listen intently, he kept his gaze focused on the flames.

She swallowed, then continued. "There was not enough food for all. The men tried to hunt, but the season was poor that year. Game was scarce." Her stare lowered to the fire. "So much crying. I remember going to sleep many times with no more than a cup of *wukuikum* and a handful of dried *bokum* all day."

"Tea and sunflower seeds?" Lance peered up at her, his face awash with dismay. "What happened to the supplies from the government?"

Winter Magic thought for a minute. "I do not know. It is my belief that the government agent for the Indians does not walk with honor . . . but I cannot say this for certain."

"Why didn't you report him?"

"Do you think your president would believe us over his own agent?"

Pursing his lips, Lance shook his head. "No, I suppose he wouldn't."

"That is what we thought, also."

"So you petitioned for a piece of land and obtained permission to start your own ranch instead of causing trouble?"

She dipped her head. "Throughout the winter I had listened to the men talking. They frightened me. They had plans to take us off the reservation and into the mountains."

"Why didn't they?"

"I gave them a better plan."

"*You* did? I didn't think women were allowed to sit in on such things."

"They are not." Winter Magic smiled. It had always made her feel good about herself to have been the one to have come up with the idea of the ranch, but now for this man to know made it all the better somehow.

"So how'd you do it?"

"I read in the Reno paper—"

"You can read?" His brows shot upward.

Not meaning to, she puffed out her chest with pride and nodded. "A friend taught me." She could see that he was impressed. "The papers spoke of the land grants given to anyone who would homestead the Nevada Territory and improve the land. And since we were people, and willing to work to keep that which was by rights already ours—"

"I see." He smiled, his gaze rising to meet hers. "That was a pretty calculating move."

"Calculating? I do not understand this word."

He chuckled softly. "Smart—it means you were pretty sly to come up with such an idea."

"It was our only chance. The soldiers would have only come after us if we had fled into the mountains. And if they had not, there were always the renegades of the Bannock to worry about." She shrugged. "It was our only chance."

"So you got the land and started your own ranch."

Pride marking her posture, she smiled. "For a while we were doing very well. We caught wild mustangs, broke them, and sold them to the army. It was not a lot, but we were content. Then the Pogonip came."

"The horse."

"*Pisha'*." Why was he still confused? "He is a horse of nobility—a barb left from the days when the Spanish walked among us."

Lance squinted at her. "You seem to know a lot about this animal."

"I have learned much. I have a friend in your Reno who has helped me to study about them."

"The same one that taught you how to read?" Again, he appeared impressed.

She nodded. "We thought if we could catch him, we could join his blood with our wild stock and have a fine ranch of breeding—like the Triple-T."

"I see." He stared into the fire, a look of realization marking his features. "So that's why El was so mad when I mentioned seeing Tunupiuts. He sees you as a rival."

"Rival?" Winter Magic had never thought of the Run of the Red Deer as being competition for the Triple-T.

"Don't you see?" Lance lifted his open hands. "If you're able to breed a better quality of stock and still sell them at a lesser cost, you'll be taking business away from the Triple-T.''

''This is not good.'' Winter Magic did not care for the Taggerts, this she had never made a secret. But to hurt their livelihood . . . she had not considered this. ''We do not wish to tear away that which your family has built. We only wish to regain our pride—to live in happiness with the white man. We are not allowed to govern ourselves, but this—it is a start.''

Lance lifted a stare. He appeared to be in agony over his own thoughts. ''It may be more than just a means to gain back your pride, Winter Magic. It may be that this valley truly does have the makings of a full-fledged war cultivating within it.''

6

Throughout the night Lance tossed in a fitful sleep. Visions of a woman with nut-brown eyes and heady laughter tumbled down into his dreams. Waist-length hair, dark as the evening sky, fell across his skin, teasing his senses. Neme. His wife had come to him again. Firelight illuminated the scene, yet he could not see her face clearly. Why? He strained, but her features were still distorted.

Her gentle hands caressed his body, trailing over the full length of him with an arousing warmth he had not experienced in a long time. Her fingers twined with his, then moved on again, exploring, coaxing, lifting him to a shuddering height of passion.

He held his breath. He was afraid to move—afraid she would vanish like she always did. God, let her stay with me this time.

His father's face leapt between them. "Damn Indian-lover!"

Neme screamed.

The snarling man above him snatched her away.

"*Kai—kai*! Lance loves me," Neme whimpered.

"Loves you?" his father's voice gnashed. "He left you, didn't he? You were just a toy—a diversion. He can't bear the sight of you anymore."

A bullwhip cracked, and somewhere in the shadows a baby cried.

"Help me!" Neme shrieked.

Lance struggled to rise, but something held him down. He could feel his wife's scalding tears. "Damn you! Damn you to hell!" he yelled at his father. Within a hueless haze he could see the man grinning. Neme held a squirming bundle.

A thick cloud of smoke closed around them. Another scream, then flames. Hot, burning, leaping, they seared his flesh. Lance tried to break through the wall of fire, but it beat him back.

"Don't leave me!" Neme cried out for him again.

Where was she? He could not see her any longer.

As if the devil himself had sprung up from hell, wicked laughter shot out from the fierce bowels of heat. A face from the past loomed out at him. Drew Jordan. Metal flashed. Pain sliced his eye. Lance grabbed his face. Blood—so much blood. A guttural noise strained his throat, but no sound escaped. Shielding himself from the white-hot blaze, he staggered backward.

"Lance!"

The strangled scream of his wife wrenched him awake. Chest heaving, he bolted upright. Fear clutched his heart. He looked around. Where was Neme?

Flames from a small campfire crackled in front of him. His upturned saddle lay behind him, his holstered gun leaning against it.

Slowly he focused on his surroundings, and his senses took command. Gray-blue, the sky had just now given up its darkness. Clean and crisp, the scent of sagebrush cleared his head. It was just a dream—another nightmare. Exhausted, he fell back to the ground. He wiped the sweat from his face.

God in heaven, why had he left Neme? His thoughts taunted him further. If only he had taken her and the baby with him to Sacramento.

His eye throbbed beneath the patch. Lifting a hand, he shielded the pain with the crook of his arm. If only his father had not hated Indians so much. If only Lance had tried harder. Securing his bedroll over his chest, he sighed.

If only her people had not been blinded by their own prejudices. If only everyone had understood how much they had loved each other and had left them alone, none of this would have happened. He squeezed his eyes closed. If only she had not chosen to die. If only . . .

Water rippled nearby. A soft moan drew his attention. Turning his head, he peeked out from beneath his arm.

Steam rose up from a thin wall of reeds swaying in the breeze.

In the dismal light a movement caught his eye. He peered over his holster lying beside his head and squinted deeper, through the curtain of willows and cattails edging the stream.

Black hair cascaded over red-brown skin. A woman's slender shoulders dipped and rose beneath the gurgling pool of the hot springs.

His mind tormented his emotions. Neme?

Her back to him, the woman lifted the length of her hair and twisted it in a knot against her head. Holding it in place with one hand, she sank deeper, up to her neck.

Unconsciously he compared this Indian woman to his Neme. Sharp and angular, her features were the exact opposite of his late wife's. Neme had been the gentlest of women. Beautiful, soft, and loving. This woman did not possess the same qualities as she, yet there was something about her that appealed to him.

Water splashed. The woman moaned again.

The sound reignited Lance's unfulfilled need for his wife. His blood heated. His gaze swept the woman for a closer inspection. Watching her, he imagined the remembered touch of Neme's body next to his. His groin tightened.

The woman bobbed in the lapping water again. Liquid sluiced off of her like sweat with each upsurge. And with every movement, a throaty whisper of breath would escape her in a rush.

Envious of the reeds that touched her skin, his fingers ached to take their place. Oh, God. With a laborious exhale, he groaned. It was more than he could bear. Her bewitching features took form behind his lids.

Her sensuous stare teased his restraint. Clinging damp against her body, wisps of hair emphasized the bold magnificence of her naked curves—full and lush, inviting his hands.

Consciously he knew the woman bathing in the spring was Winter Magic—not Neme—but his need had grown too strong. The name no longer mattered.

Liquid-fire raced through his veins. He felt himself harden. His body's demands became unbearable. His heart pounded. His control had all but diminished. His hand tightened into fists.

"Ganoida bui?"

Lance flinched. He jerked down his arm.

Winter Magic knelt beside him, her body draped half across him. Glistening wet, dark-lashed eyes peered down at him. "You were moaning. You are ill?"

A single droplet of water drew his attention. Following it, his gaze slid from the edge of one brow, over her cheek, to the corner of her full mouth. He felt the cool downpour of her hair spill over her shoulder and onto his neck. He dipped his chin forward. Dropping his line of vision to where it pooled within his open shirt, he sucked in a breath.

It swept back and forth on the light breeze, the damp ends doing more to set his body ablaze than to douse it. Caught off guard, the sight sparked the most primitive of his emotions. It was all he could do to exercise control. His face broke out in a sheen of sweat. He sent a prayer heavenward.

"Lance?" She laid her hand on his chest.

Hell answered his plea instead. Her touch flamed his smoldering senses into a full brushfire. He met her anxious look with an emblazoned stare.

"You are feeling bad?"

Her concern only served to feed his desire. He shook his head.

Her brows drew together. "What is wrong with you, then?"

His baser need seized him. Reaching up, he brushed away a bead of water running down her chin with his knuckles. Her skin felt cool, dewy. He trailed his hand up to her hair, then combed his fingers down its length.

She shuddered beneath his touch, the single action returning his attention to her body.

His gaze fell heavy on the ample swell of her breasts. Wet and bare beneath the thin material of her shirt, they clung to the white fabric of her blouse. His muscles thickened. He swallowed. He allowed his fantasy to take control. "You're so beautiful. Neme."

The woman smiled cautiously, bewilderment stalking the dark allure of her eyes. She pressed down on his chest with a slight shake. "You are still sleeping, Ganoida bui. You are dreaming. Wake up now."

"Is *this* a dream?" He recaptured her face. He slid his hand up to the back of her neck and pulled her head down.

She tensed. Like black lightning, her eyes flashed terror. She struggled, pushing away from him. "*Kai*!"

His arms locked tight around her. "It's been so long. And I need you so bad. Don't fight me." The words rushed against her mouth.

"I am not your Neme!" she said with force, her voice quaking. She shot a punch to his kidneys with a fist.

Startled from his reverie, his hand still tangled in her hair, he blinked.

Her nails dug into his side. "I am Winter Magic."

Seconds whirled past as he stared up at her. He panted. With each rush of breath a blow of realization struck. The woman spoke the truth. She wasn't Neme. His grip went slack. His fingers flexed. But the terrible rage of need would not release him. Gently he cupped the back of her neck with his hand.

Lips trembling, the woman did not stir.

He lifted her hair, just a little, then stroked her skin with his thumb. "I know who you are. You're Winter Magic." He paused. "And . . . I need you."

He encircled her again, forcing her fully across him, cinching their bodies together. His lips crushed hers.

Her eyes sprang wide. She struggled and squirmed, flailing against his body.

Finding her arms, Lance gripped her wrists, drawing them up behind her. He did not want to hurt her, but the animal lust snarling within him was too powerful. He had to have this woman.

She wrenched her mouth away. "*Kai*, Lance. Please. You must not. Do not do this to me."

He clamped one hand around hers, then reached up and curved his fingers around her throat.

She gasped, then stilled. Her eyes lit with terror. Then just as quickly, they darkened to a shadow of rage. "You are hurting me, Lance Taggert," she grated between clenched teeth.

What was he doing? He pulled back. He was furious with himself for frightening her. Would he really have forced himself on her? He loosened his grip on her hands, but not his embrace. He eased his head back to the ground and stroked her jawline with his thumb. "I didn't mean to hurt you."

Winter Magic braced herself upright atop his chest. She glared hard at him. At first she appeared angry, but after another moment her temper fell away. She looked as if she understood his pain—as if she, too, knew the need of a lost lover. The fear and fury in her eyes softened to compassion. She did not move. Why did she remain on top of him?

Fire still raging through his body, he forced himself to relax. He averted his gaze. He could not look at her. "It's just that it's been so damn long. And you're so beautiful." Strange. When had he started thinking of her like that? He felt her swallow.

"I am not blind to your pain, Lance Taggert."

Her words only increased his torment. "It's all right, Winter Magic. I'm okay now."

"It is good that you are brave, but it is not needed with me. I, too, know the sorrow of an empty heart."

His eyes found her face again. Did she speak the truth? How did she know? Had she lost someone, too? It did not matter. He did not care. He only knew how *he* felt and what *he* needed. He could not help himself. His lust jolted to life again.

He worked his thumb across the gentle pulse in her throat. "Why do you have to be so understanding, so alive, and . . ." He lifted his head, then hesitated inches from her lips. "So beautiful?" Damn his lusting appetite. He could not stop himself. He closed his eyes. He found the back of her head and pulled her down to meet his crushing kiss.

Her heart pounded against his chest—or was it her fist? It spurred his passion. What game did she play? It did not matter. He could not stop himself. Drunk on the adrenaline flooding his senses, he would not allow her body to break contact with his again.

He flicked his tongue through the tightness of her lips.

She tensed again. "*Kai*, Lance, do not—" A scream strangled in her throat. Her muscles tightened.

He flinched. He wanted her, but not like this. He had to control his actions—to reassure her fears. He suddenly wanted her to enjoy this as much as he. Easing up, he softened the kiss, but did not pull away.

Slow and steady he coursed the full pout of her bottom lip. It trembled against his touch. In fact, everything about her trembled. Through a hooded gaze, he thought he saw a flash of sympathetic longing in her eyes. He felt a momentary stab of resentment, but pushed it aside. Charity, or not, he would take her anyway she would let him.

Timidly her tongue met his.

Why *had* she stopped fighting him? He leaned back and looked at her. Was she feeling sorry for him?

She lifted her head.

Their eyes met.

She appeared uncertain—almost fearful again.

Moments passed. Raw passion stalked the silence.

His mind railed at him to reassure her, but his body would not. He had pushed too far. He was crazy with the need of her. Did she want him, too? His heart thundered the burning question.

Hers answered, matching his, thud for painful thud.

They met in a rush. Gloriously demanding, their mouths devoured each other's.

He pulled her fully on top of him. Hard and fast, her breathing set the tempo of the storm raging within him.

He splayed his fingers across the small of her back, pressing her hips against his groin. White-hot, the single action jarred his senses.

She moaned, deep in her throat. Her hands slid under his head. Clutching his hair, she dug one knee into his thigh. Her breasts pillowed firm through the thin barrier of their shirts.

He broke away from the kiss, trailing a path down her jawline to her neck. He seared the tiny throb pulsing just below her ear with a graze of his tongue. She tasted cool, clean, hot, and womanly sweet all at once.

It was more than he could stand. Breathless, he backed off once more—but just long enough to move. He rolled above her.

With unbridled abandon, she jerked his shirt out from the waistband of his pants. Her hands slid under his clothing along his spine.

He groaned hard against her mouth. The shock of her icy fingers against his skin charged him with excitement.

Her touch was everywhere—kneading, scratching, pulling him closer.

He knew he should slow down, but he could not hold back any longer. He rocked the painful ache of his shaft against her.

She met him with a thrust of her own.

He moved to unfasten his pants, then reached for hers.

She tensed.

He eased up. "I'm sorry. I can't wait," he whispered against her ear. "It'll be better next time." He released the first two buttons.

She did not move.

Lifting his head, he met her wide-eyed stare. What had he done? She could not be a virgin. If that were true, she would not have become so willing so quick.

An animal snorted. His body went rigid. He peered up. Kozo and the ranch horse stood tethered a good distance in front of them. His awareness came slow, then bolted when another movement sounded behind them.

They were no longer alone.

Winter Magic remained immobile. Her eyes rounded as she stared over Lance Taggert's shoulder. Two men sat astride horses only a few feet away from where she lay beneath the white man. She did not need to see their faces to know they had to be from the Triple-T.

Lance grabbed his gun from the holster lying next to his saddle. He lunged up, positioning himself between her and the men.

"There's no call for the Colt, Lance," Shea Taggert called out. He shifted uncomfortably in his seat. "It's me and El."

Winter Magic scrambled to her feet. Embarrassed heat swept her face and throat as she struggled to adjust her clothing.

Lance darted a nervous look over his shoulder. He shifted his stance, shielding her protectively from his brothers' view with his body. Resetting the hammer safely on his pistol, he reholstered the weapon, then straightened his own clothes. "What're you two doing out here?"

After nudging their horses forward, the two men reined their mounts just short of Lance.

"You didn't—uh—" Shea swallowed. "I mean— I'm—uh—sorry 'bout ridin' up on you like this, but . . . Well, you didn't come home last night."

Tucking her shirt back into her pants, Winter Magic caught the intruding brothers looking at her.

Obviously feeling as much discomfort as she, Shea cut his gaze back to Lance.

But Eldon Taggert did not. He leaned forward and rested a forearm atop his saddle horn, his eyes fixed on hers, a leer lifting one corner of his mouth.

Winter Magic shuddered. What would happen now? She steadied her breathing. She could not let him see how frightened he made her.

Shea started to dismount. "Stumpy told us you took off yesterday mornin' not long after we did."

Lance backed closer to Winter Magic.

Shea halted mid-action. Then, cautiously, he stepped down from the stirrup, his hands held out from his sides. "We thought somethin' might've happened to you." He took a step forward.

Lance met his movement. "Yeah, like what?" He sounded angry.

Winter Magic swallowed. Would the Ganoida

bui really protect her from his own brothers if they tried anything? And there was no doubt in her mind that they would. Maybe not Shea, but Eldon . . . Feeling the man's lingering stare, she cringed.

"Ah, hell, Lance—I don't know. Anythin'." Shea set a gloved hand atop the opposite hip from his gun. "We were worried's all."

"Guess we didn't need to be, though, eh, Lance?" Eldon Taggert tossed a lustful wink at his brother, then nodded toward Winter Magic.

Feeling a stab of true fear, she shivered, partly from the cold, more from the man's insinuating gesture.

"What's that suppose to mean?" Lance said in a grating voice.

"Nothin'." Shea glared at Eldon before looking back at Lance. "He didn't mean anythin', did you, El?" Caution marked his tone.

"The hell I didn't!" Eldon Taggert threw his leg over his saddle and slipped down to stand facing Winter Magic. He slapped the reins lightly against the gloved palm of his hand. "You just can't stay away from these squaws, can you, little brother?"

"El! Don't start anything." Shea glowered at the older man.

"I ain't starting nothin'. Hell, I'd pin this one down myself if I got the chance."

Lance flexed his hands, balling them into fists. His posture tensed.

"Shut up, El," Shea warned. "We didn't come out here lookin' for trouble."

"Good." Lance's words clipped the air. "You

came out to find me. Thanks. I'm okay, so why don't you go on back home."

"Sure . . . no problem." Shea quirked a nervous smile. "Come on, El, let's go."

But Eldon Taggert ignored his youngest brother. He focused his sights on Winter Magic. "Oh, yeah. You're great, Lance," he sneered. "You're home one day. You get a twitch in your pants, and you take care of it with the first Indian gal you run across. I guess we're more alike than I figured."

"El!" Shea turned his back on Lance and grabbed his oldest brother's arm.

Shaking off the man's hand, Eldon riveted his stare to Winter Magic. "Relax." He grinned, but his eyes gleaned a different emotion.

She darted a fearful glance toward Kozo. Too far. She remembered her knife. Her heart lodged in her throat. She had left it with her jacket beside the spring. She took an instinctive step backward.

Eldon moved a pace nearer.

Like a crack of lightning, Lance jerked out his gun. He pointed it at Eldon's chest.

Silence rode down on the group.

Then, just as suddenly, Eldon burst into laughter. "What the hell's that for?"

Lance flicked the barrel up. "You're not going to touch her."

Eldon sobered. One hand resting heavy on the coil of a bullwhip fastened at his waist, he stared at his brother for a long minute. He appeared to be sizing up Lance's bravado.

"I mean it, El. You and Shea get out of here—now!"

Neither moved.

Locked in a war of stares, the two eldest men remained motionless, waging their own battle of wills.

Shea darted an agitated glance between them.

Winter Magic held her breath.

Eldon moved first, startling them all. He whipped up the reins of his horse's lead and slapped them across his hand. His earlier grin returned. "Sure, Lance. Whatever you say. . . ." He turned away.

Too quick to see it coming, Winter Magic only heard the sound.

Leather cracked like thunder.

The gun flew out of Lance's hand. He grabbed his wrist.

Eldon jerked up his arm, and Winter Magic saw it. The coil of the man's bullwhip lashed backward. He threw it out again.

She screamed, but it served no purpose. The strength of the braided snake caught Lance full-force across the face.

7

Wide-eyed, Winter Magic watched helplessly. She covered her mouth with her hands.

Eldon Taggert's lips curled in a hideous smirk. With the expertise of a skilled lash-master, he drew back his arm. The whip cracked. Again and again, it flew up only to be unleashed still another time. It struck once more and caught Lance across the back.

Ducking and dodging, he tried to avoid the sting of the lash, but it caught him, shredding his thick jacket with a savage bite.

"Shea!" Winter Magic screamed. Her stare darted to the younger man.

He appeared chiseled in solid rock.

She pitched to his side, grabbing his arm. "Do something. He will kill Lance."

Still he did not move.

"Shea!" She shook him.

Turning to look at her, he blinked.

She pointed at Lance. "Help him!" she commanded.

The whip sang again, and Lance fell to his knees. Blood trickled from the gash across his cheek.

Shea bolted forward. The sound of an ancient war cry tore from his lungs. He slammed, full body, into Eldon Taggert. The men crashed onto the snow-covered ground.

The older brother leapt to his feet. He raised the whip, but Shea moved too quick.

He rolled away from the strike. He jumped up and charged the man again.

Winter Magic ran to Lance. She fell down beside him.

Bent over, he held himself rigid. Blood and snow, mud and sweat smeared his features.

Tears stung Winter Magic's eyes. Lifting his head, she smoothed a dark lock of hair from his forehead. "Oh, Lance," she whimpered.

Another crack of leather peeled the air.

Over her shoulder she darted the fighting men a fearful glance.

Shea caught the end of the lash around his wrist. He winced but held his stance. Twisting his hand, he coiled the thong around his arm and yanked.

But Eldon Taggert was too powerful. He gripped the handle with both hands and jerked against Shea's hold, pulling him to the ground. He ran to the younger man. "Let go!" Wrenching and tugging, beating Shea with the braided hilt, he freed the leather.

Shea rolled to his side. He grabbed the older man's foot, pitching him into the snow.

Eldon Taggert groaned. He drew back his leg. A boot flew up, smashing into Shea's face.

Without warning, Lance bolted upright. In a rage he lunged at his older brother, ramming the man's back with the full impact of his shoulder.

Shea lunged to his feet. He sprang at his battling brothers.

Like wild beasts, the men snarled. They tumbled over each other, no one man distinguishable from the other. Fists bashing faces, punching stomachs, battering bodies.

Winter Magic hugged herself. She had witnessed many fights between many men, but this was too much. This struggle was because of her. She wanted to help, but what could she do? She looked around for someone—anyone who could end this.

Her gaze found a discarded pistol. Rushing to it, she picked it up and pulled back the hammer. She held her breath. She did not like guns, but this had to be stopped—now! Bracing her stance, she pointed the weapon at the sky and pulled the trigger. Thunder roared. Then silence.

The men froze.

Chest heaving, she cocked the hammer again. She lowered the gun, leveling it on them. "No more!" she spat breathlessly. "You will fight no more."

For another moment all remained still.

Eldon Taggert moved first. Rising to his feet, he inched toward his bullwhip.

"Stop!" Winter Magic would not allow the fighting to begin again. Her hands were cold, near freezing in the dry, frost-bitten air, but she held on to the weapon for all her worth.

He hesitated, then grinned. "You going to shoot me, squaw?"

Winter Magic cringed. She hated the sound of that word. It would be so easy to pull the trigger and end all of this. If she were to kill Eldon Taggert, the hatred in the valley would die with him.

But there are others, her inner voice reminded her. He has many friends—like Garret Samuels, Moon Dove's husband. Will you kill him as well? No. She could not do that. She must find another way to end this war of hatred between her people and the whites. The gun wavered in her hand.

Fingers spread, Eldon Taggert bent down for the whip.

She squeezed the trigger. The gun exploded.

Eldon Taggert recoiled.

She missed her target by a good length of a man's stride. She had no skill with this weapon, but she could not let him know that. "Move away—back to the others."

Pushing themselves up from the ground, Lance and Shea stared at her.

"Well—*squaw*. Now that you've got all of us, what're you aiming to do with us?" Eldon Taggert grated with a hate-filled glower.

Winter Magic hesitated. What *was* she going to do? She gestured toward the horses with a wave of the pistol. "You will leave."

"Sure, squaw. Whatever you—" He reached for his gun, but the holster was empty.

Winter Magic glanced down at the weapon in her hand. She smiled pointedly. She had not known until now whose Colt she had. A surge of confidence filled her being. "Now. You *will* leave."

Eldon Taggert glared at her long and hard.

"Now!" Her breath puffed from her body in a little cloud of white. She would not let his anger back her down.

"C'mon," he said to his brothers. He snatched up his hat and moved toward his horse. "Let's get the hell outta here before that squaw-bitch lets another bullet fly."

"*Kai*. They will follow." She did not trust Eldon Taggert. Shea and Lance would wait to leave until he had gone.

The eldest of the three brothers glared at Winter Magic. "You goin' to let her tell you what to do like that?" He gestured at her with a dismissing wave.

Brushing the snow from his pant legs, Lance branded him with a burning expression. "Best you do like the woman says."

Eldon Taggert looked to Shea.

The younger man nodded. "She does have your gun."

Darting one last glare at each of them, Eldon Taggert jerked up his horse's reins, mounted, and rode off in the direction of the Triple-T.

Still holding the gun, Winter Magic's hands began to shake. Except for her tussle with Lance two days earlier, she had never held a weapon on anyone. Adrenaline slowing, she shivered, the nipping cold reminding her of her need for heat.

On stiff legs she hurried to the campfire. She sat the gun down on the bedroll where Lance had slept. Like a wooden doll she retrieved her jacket, pulled it on, then knelt and held her hands up to the flames.

She stared into the small blaze. So much had

happened—and all since she had met Lance Taggert.

A hand touched her shoulder. "Are you okay?" The sound of Lance's voice soothed her—yet disturbed her more than she would have liked.

The wind blew a haunting breath across her face. She looked up. Sometime during the battle, he had lost his patch and for the first time, Winter Magic gazed upon the stark beauty and cruel tragedy of his pain.

Whiter than a shade of moonlight, his injured eye stared back at her. The chilling breeze ruffled the hair falling across his brow. She groaned inwardly.

Why did she feel so close to this man so soon? She knew almost nothing of him, nor his past, yet something was drawing them together. Why? Was he truly sent by the Great Spirit? It was all too quick—too confusing. If so, she was not meant to get involved with him. She was only to learn from him. She had much too much to do for her people. She was responsible for getting them started in the ways of the white world, and she must see things through.

A man—any man—but especially a white man too deeply embedded in her life would only complicate matters. She had no time for frivolous dealings. And after Owl Eyes— She gave herself a mental shake. She would not allow anything like that to happen again.

And if Lance truly was the sign she had asked the Great Spirit to send, what was the lesson she was supposed to learn from the man? Thinking of their earlier tryst, she shook her head and squeezed her eyes closed. What lesson indeed.

Looking at him again, she nodded in answer of his question. *"Pisha'.* I am unharmed." Her gaze scanned his bleeding face. Her heart tightened. With light and caring fingers she grazed the arch of the brow over his left eye. She hesitated near the slash on his cheek. "But you, Lance Taggert—"

He flinched, but shook his head. Taking her hand in his, he gifted her with a weak smile. "It's just a scratch." His thumb stroked her knuckles.

For a long moment they sat silently gazing at each other, their eyes speaking of heart-felt gratitude, their touch speaking of more.

"Thanks for helping us, Winter Magic." Shea Taggert joined them by the fireside, his usual infectious smile splitting a now battered face. "I hadn't realized how tough you'd grown up to be."

A flash of memory goaded her attention. She and Shea had found each other in the desert as children and had played together on many occasions. They were not really friends, but he was the only Taggert she had never considered an enemy. "It is good to see you again, also."

He nodded with a grin. "Nothing like a rowdy game of cowboys and Indians to get your blood surging first thing in the morning, is there?"

Winter Magic took in a slow breath. He had meant it as a joke, she was certain, but his comment caused only sadness within her. She looked back at Lance. Remembering her hand, she withdrew from his touch. "I must go."

"Now?" Lance asked.

"Pisha'. My uncle will be waiting for me." Taking up her knife from beside the fire, she stood, then strapped it to her hip.

"I'll ride with you—to make sure you get home okay." Rising, Lance moved to where the black patch lay in the snow. He appeared suddenly uncomfortable with her watchfulness. He retrieved the covering and replaced it over his eye.

Why did he do that? It was too beautiful to keep hidden. Did it still cause him pain? "*Kai*, Lance. I will go alone."

Ignoring her comment, he returned to his bedroll, picked up the blanket, then shook it free of snow. After winding it in a bundle, he met her stare. "You ready?"

Had he not understood her? She peered deeper. Why did he not listen? His returning with her would only make trouble. Friend or not, Nighthawk would not be kind in his understanding.

Winter Magic lowered her gaze from the white man's to the tops of her moccasins. She did not trust herself further. Her emotions might win over her reasoning. She must convince him to go back with his brother. "I am Paiute. I have traveled this valley my whole life. I will have no trouble finding my way home."

"No, of course not," the Ganoida bui said too matter-of-factly.

Winter Magic cut him a tolerant expression. "I do not think my uncle would be pleased to see us together so soon after—" She darted an embarrassed look between Shea and Lance.

A puzzled expression marked Lance's features.

"I *was* sent here to pray," she offered pointedly, hoping he would get her meaning. After all, he had been the cause of her punishment.

Lifting a brow, he dipped his head.

She gathered her pony blanket and walked to Kozo.

The two men followed behind.

After leaping atop her horse, Winter Magic looked down at Lance Taggert. "One day maybe you *will* come to our ranch, but for now—" Giving thought to her words, she paused. "For now it is better that you do not."

"Yeah." He appeared to understand the underlying meaning of her statement.

Their eyes met again, and somewhere deep in the pit of her stomach, she felt an unfulfilled tingle of desire tickle her senses anew. Dragging her gaze away, she urged Kozo forward, but pulled up before the animal could take a step. "I will pray that you are wrong, Lance Taggert."

Frowning, he pinned her with an inquiring look. "About what?"

"About the war you believe is coming to this valley. I will speak to my uncle. I will think on the words you spoke last night." She lifted her gaze and stared in the direction of Eldon Taggert's departure. "Maybe there is something that can be done to end it before it grows ugly and strong."

"I'll think about it, too, Tu'madai."

She shivered at the sound of him using her name so familiarly.

"Maybe." His knowing stare reached in and touched her soul. "If we combine our efforts, we might be able to bring our two peoples together so that there doesn't have to be a battle."

She was not quite certain how he meant the words *we* and *combine*. And she was not certain she wanted to find out. She said no more. There was nothing left to say—not even good-bye. Deep down, she knew she would see him again. He was the sign. If the Great Spirit had sent this warrior, maybe the Ganoida bui was correct in his thinking. Maybe white men and red alike *could* find a way to live and work together in this valley. If only she knew for certain he had been the warrior sent to help her people.

High above a lone hawk shrieked.

She looked up, shielding her eyes with her hand from the sun's glare reflecting off the snow. Catching sight of the bird, she took a reassuring breath. Red and white, its feathers lay one against the other in beautiful contrast, yet perfectly blended. She had her answer.

Her stare flitted downward to Lance. The Great Spirit was indeed wise. The Ganoida bui *had* been sent to show them the way. Maybe they could combine their efforts. Maybe . . .

Lance watched Winter Magic ride off to the north. He felt relief with her departure, yet he did not want her to go. Why? Hell, he didn't even know her. He glanced down at the spot that had served as his bed. And what about earlier? He had nearly compromised her—not to mention himself. Had he gone without a woman that long? No. He had taken his pleasures. But not often, and only when the need had been too strong to resist.

Yeah, he told himself. That's all she'd been—a remedy for his pent-up lust. Yet, since Neme, his desires had not hit him as powerfully as it had that morning. Maybe that was it. She was Indian and he was home. Old feelings die hard—and the passion he felt for his wife was far from dead. Yeah. Winter Magic had only served as a reminder of that fact. Nothing more.

"You all right?"

Lance blinked. He straightened the patch over his eye. "Yeah. I'm fine." Barely able to see the woman now, he turned to face his brother. "Guess we ought to get on back to the ranch."

"Yup." Shea snorted. "I got to tell you, though. I'm not looking forward to seein' El no time too soon."

"Yeah, well—" Lance slapped Shea on the back good-naturedly. "We'll ride slow."

"Suits me fine."

Lance saddled his horse while Shea put out the fire with handfuls of snow.

"So. What about you and Winter Magic?" Shea asked casually after they had been mounted and riding a short distance.

"Nothing much to tell. I met her on the ride in from Reno. She's Tunupiuts's niece." Lance shifted uncomfortably in his saddle. He did not want to discuss the Indian woman.

Shea dipped his head. "I know who she is. Sure is something how you two got to know each other so quick."

"Drop it, Shea."

The younger man chuckled. "Sorry. I was just making conversation's all."

Lance did not reply. He had to steer clear of this subject. And for him, constraint would be the best move.

Except for the chomping of snow made by the horses' steps, a silence stretched between the men.

After a while he became aware of some curious glances shot at him by Shea. Damn, but he was sick of people always staring and feeling sorry for him. He might not be able to do anything about it with others, but he would not tolerate it from his own brother. Perturbed, he took the initiative. "Why don't you just ask and get it over with, Shea?"

"Ask what?"

"About my eye?"

"Sorry." Shea sounded sincere. "I didn't mean to keep starin'."

Lance released a heavy sigh. He knew someone would want to know about the incident concerning his eye before too long. He had prepared himself for this all the way out from Chicago.

"Okay, so . . . how'd it happen?"

"A fight." Lance found himself still a little reluctant to talk about the circumstances.

Shea frowned. "I know I was little when you left home, but I always remember you as bein' able to hold your own—even with El. I heard you were one of the agency's finest. How is it you let somebody get the best of you?"

"Sometimes even the most experienced don't see things coming." That had been the most truth he had said about the incident since it had occurred.

"So where'd this happen?"

Lance cut Shea a tolerant look. "I was on a job for the governor in a town just south of here. A little place called Cavenaugh's Dig up in the gold country."

"You were involved with that monitor trouble? I heard about all that ruckus with them water cannons. Can they really tear down the whole side of a mountain?"

"Damn close."

Shea whistled. "I'd like to see that."

How many times since the accident had Lance wished he had never seen any of them? Too many. "It's not a very pretty sight."

"No doubt. Still . . ." Shea cocked his head to one side. "So how'd you get hurt again? You said it was a fight?"

Lance took a deep breath. Everything came back to him at once. The huge pit, the water cannons spitting their blasts of water, the explosion, the knife flashing in the brilliant sun—everything. But most of all, he recalled the man. He had not thought it would cause so much torment to remember the details. "I caught the bastard that had been sabotaging all the mining equipment red-handed." Lost in the memory, a twinge of pain stabbed his eye. He flinched. If he had only seen him sooner . . . If he had only been quicker—

"Yup. I read about the string of disasters. The Reno newspapers said it was one of the owner's sons."

Lance cringed inwardly. "Drew Jordan," he grated between clenched teeth. Remembering the man twice in one twenty-four-hour period was too much. Hell, remembering him at all was too much.

"Damn!" Shea sounded excited. "Was it always like that working undercover? What other kind of adventures did you have?"

Didn't he care that Lance had been hurt? Lance shot his brother an injured glare. Was that all he wanted to hear about—adventure?

"Sorry." Shea ducked his head like a scolded boy. "That was pretty unfeelin' of me. I didn't mean to ignore what happened to you. How bad did you get hurt? Can you see at all? Does it still cause you pain?"

Lance felt somewhat appeased. "I can see a little. The surgery gave me that. But it's all blurry—just moving images really."

"That's great!" Shea's voice pitched eagerly.

"Not to me, it's not."

"You'll think different once you're back workin' for the governor again."

Lance shook his head. It had been a hard decision to make—worse to accept—but now that he had made it, he was going to stick to it. "I'm not going back."

"What?" Shea reined his animal short. He turned to stare at Lance. "What're you talkin' about? Of course you're goin' back. You just need some time to rest—get your mind straight."

Halting his mount beside his brother, Lance met the challenge in the younger man's eyes. "My mind *is* straight. I'm not going back."

"Why in hell not? That little cut make you scared all of a sudden?"

"Little cut!" Lance's insides twisted.

Startled, Shea jumped.

"Hell, boy, I barely came away from that fight alive." Lance hated the thought of losing the hero worship of the younger man, but he had to tell him the truth. "To do the job I did, and do it well, a man needs all his faculties—wits, smell, hearing, touch, sight—everything. Otherwise, he could find himself dead. All you see is the seduction. Well, what about the danger? Have you considered that?''

Jaws tight, he pulled up his shirt to expose a small pattern of old scars splaying across his side. "Shotgun, seven years ago. Still carrying a piece of a forty-four slug I caught in my shoulder while on a special assignment with President Johnson.''

"You still got one good eye.''

"It's not enough.'' Pent-up anger surged his blood. The governor had told him the same thing, almost word for word, when Lance had resigned. "You haven't been in the situations I have—you don't understand.''

Shea stared hard at his brother, his look riddled with surprise. "So explain it.''

"I just did!'' Frustrated, Lance did not know what else to say. He felt as if he had been gut-kicked, as if he had somehow let his kid brother down, but he had to tell him the facts—painful as they were. And if Shea could not understand, well . . . There was nothing Lance could do about it.

A small glimmer of light grew to a sparkle in Shea's eyes. He seemed to read what Lance was thinking. "President Johnson, huh?''

Dumbfounded, Lance could only stare. The younger man could only see the adventure and excitement of the job, but none of the hazards. He shook his head with a snort.

"So. You think it'd be hard for someone like me to land a position with the governor's office?''

Lance pulled a frown. Was he serious? A slow grin tugged at the corners of his mouth. He had all but forgotten the spontaneous energy of youth. "It's possible. We'll talk about it later." Tapping the horse's flanks, he urged the animal forward again.

Shea followed suit.

"So." Lance decided to turn the table on Shea. "How's that pretty little Chloe Summerhorn doing?"

Shea's face reddened, but he put on a good show of indifference. "She's okay, I guess."

"You guess? You were pretty sweet on her last I recall."

"I was only fourteen."

"Seems to me I heard that you got rock salt shot in your backside by her pa the last time you slipped over there to see her at night."

"Lance." Shea's voice hinted of warning, as well as suppressed amusement.

"Didn't anyone ever teach you how to be quiet when you went window-sparking?"

Shea chuckled. "Hell, no. You think I'da stood around and let that ol' coot shoot me in the butt like that if somebody had?"

They laughed together.

Lance sobered. "You still see her?"

"Not for about seven years now. Her family sent her back East to some fancy girl's school in Boston."

"She doesn't ever come home?"

Shea shook his head. "We write—but it's not the same as gettin' to talk in person."

"You two ever plan on settling down sometime?"

Shea shrugged. "Things like that are hard to know when you can't ever get together."

"Her pa still holding that grudge against you for her little brother's accident?"

"Yup. Still thinks I was responsible."

"You were only six yourself. You couldn't know Jerome was going to fall into that nest of rattlers."

"I know. But Seth Summerhorn didn't see it that way. He thought since I was a few months older, I should have known what was going on. He didn't understand that we were both just two little boys playing with what we thought was a bunch of jumping worms." He expelled a heavy sigh. "He's hated me ever since. And when Chloe and I started seein' each other . . . well, that just made things all the worse."

Rounding the eastern side of the lake, both men stopped their horses and fell silent.

Lance looked out at the expanse of barbed-wire fencing encircling the ranch. His gaze came to rest on Ol' Char and the graves of his parents beneath it. The old feelings crept up on him again. He should never have left Neme and the baby. He should never have listened to his father. He should have known the man was up to something when he offered to keep an eye on them while Lance was in Sacramento. His heart tightened. His body tensed.

"If Chloe's what you want, Shea," he kept his gaze leveled on the burial ground across the lake, "and if you're what she wants, you two can't let her pa stop you from being together."

Shea dipped his head, but his eyes remained steady on his brother. "You goin' to visit them?"

Lance shrugged. "Maybe later."

After another moment of stilted quiet, Shea spoke again. "I know what Pa did to you and Neme, Lance. I think he felt real bad about it later, after you'd left and all."

Lance gripped the reins tighter. He did not want

to hear any of this. Alive, his father would never have sought Lance's forgiveness. But now years after the man's death Lance felt like Timothy Taggert was everywhere seeking his son's compassion. He looked back at Shea. No. Forgiveness was too great a gift to be granted to a messenger.

Heeling the horse's flanks, Lance took off in a trot, leaving Shea to follow at will. He had no time to dwell on the subject now. He focused his mind on the agreement he had made with Winter Magic. Now there were other things more pressing than the hatred he still felt for his father.

8

By the time Lance and Shea made it back to the ranch, Eldon had taken off for Reno.

"He wouldn't even talk," Stumpy told Lance after he had questioned the old man as to Eldon's whereabouts. "But I could see right plain he was pissed about something. Didn't look too good, neither. 'Bout as bad as the two a ya, matter-a-fact." Dish towel draping his middle as he stood over a boiling pot, the scruffy cook squinted at each brother in turn. "I don't s'pose either one a ya know what happened?"

"We got in a fight," Shea piped in before Lance had a chance to speak.

Stumpy hammered both men with a look as hard as steel. "The three a ya—all at once?"

"Yup." Shea crossed the kitchen to the sink and pumped some water into his hands, then splashed his face.

Stumpy chuckled. "Saw it coming—right from the start. I was jist hoping it'd wait a day or two." He tossed some ground peppers into the kettle. "So. You gonna spill the beans, or what?"

Lance darted Shea a sidelong look, commanding him to silence. He shifted his stare to Stumpy. "What did Eldon tell you?" He had no desire to discuss the morning's incident in detail if he could help it. Not that he was embarrassed—he simply saw no purpose in disclosing his personal affairs. And not that everyone would not know about it eventually—that was an unquestioned fact. But for now he chose to be discreet.

"I told ya. He didn't say a damn thing. His jaws were set tighter than a badger's bite. He jist blustered in with a huff, grabbed some money, your pa's ol' Colt, and left."

"How'd you know where he was goin', then?" Shea dabbed his face with a clean towel.

"Don't really." Stumpy picked up his miniature cuspidor and spit a mouthful of tobacco juice into it. He shrugged. "Reno's where he usually lights out to when he's pissed. He stays gone a day or so gambling, drinking, and consorting with the womenfolk at Maudy Beth's. Then he comes back in his usual good humor—such as it is."

After pulling off his coat, Lance took Shea's place at the sink. He doused his entire head, letting the water soothe his battered features. He accepted the towel from his little brother and looked up. "You got a shirt I can borrow?"

Shea swept Lance with an appraising gaze. "Might be a snug fit, but I think we can find somethin' that'll work."

"Where the hell *you* off to?" Stumpy sounded perturbed.

"Reno."

"A course ya are." He turned his back on the brothers. "And ain't I jist the damndest fool for asking, too?" He glanced over his shoulder and called out after the two men as they made for the main part of the house. "You going, too, I s'pose?" He jabbed a wooden spoon at Shea.

"Suppose so." Shea winked at Lance. "Nothin' else to do around here."

"Nothing else?" Stumpy's voice pitched. "Damn barn needs to be finished painted. We got a mare 'bout to foal. Animals that needs feeding—but there ain't nothing else to do 'round here. No, siree—nothing!"

Shaking his head, Shea slapped Lance on the back, then gestured up the stairs, with a hurry-up-and-let's-get-the-hell-out-of-here look.

But even after they had taken the steps halfway up, Lance could still hear Stumpy complaining.

"Hell, yeah. Go on and have a good time in Reno. I'll see it all gets done. Didn't want any a ya li'l cusses to try my new bean recipe anyway. Prob'ly would a jist pissed and moaned 'bout 'em being too spicy anyhow. . . ."

By late afternoon Lance and Shea had driven the wagon the full fifty odd miles from the ranch into Reno. And not once did Willful, nor the other mule that made up the team, cause Lance any trouble.

Shea pointed to a stately building trimmed in dark green. "Drop me off at the hotel there, and I'll get us a room for the night. By the time you get the wagon over to the smithy and get it set with a new whiffletree, it'll be evenin'."

Pulling up in front of the hotel, Lance nodded. He scanned the bustling street as Shea jumped out. "You think we'll be able to find El?"

"Like Stumpy said. This's where he always goes when he gets riled. He's got to be 'round here somewhere." Leaning against the wagonside, Shea glanced toward a rowdy-sounding bar at the end of the street. "How's 'bout we meet at that saloon and have a drink before we get started lookin'? Hell, it's loud enough that he may even be in there."

After that long, cold ride a shot of whiskey was just what Lance needed to warm his blood. "Sounds good."

Pushing himself away from the rig, Shea nodded. "See you in 'bout half an hour then, okay?"

"Yeah, that'll do." With a click of his tongue, Lance slapped the reins against the mules' rumps, and the buckboard lurched forward. But before he dropped off the wagon to the smithy, he drove to the train depot to pick up the luggage he had left with the stationmaster.

He checked the contents of the leather traveling bag and his other smaller cowhide case containing an expensive rifle and scope. All were as he had packed them.

He thought of the last time the weapon had been fired and of the man that had used it. His friend, Colm McQuaid. He wondered how things had worked out for the gunman and his lady, Maginn O'Shaunasey. He had received one letter from them while he was in Chicago telling of their marriage. He smiled. Always knew they would get married.

He made himself a promise to go to Sacramento and pay them a visit once things were set right at the ranch.

After he dropped off the buckboard for repairs, he set off for the hotel and left his bags in the room Shea had rented. That done, he headed for the saloon.

He crossed the street and passed an alley where two boys of about six or seven years of age played a game of shoot-'em-up.

One pointed at him with a wooden gun. "Look at that man. He's the robber." He took aim. "Bang. Bang-bang."

The suggestion the kid made did not set with Lance very well, but he did not let it show. They were only kids. He, himself, had spent many a day with his brothers playing this same game.

"Hey, mister," the second kid, a dirty-faced carrot-top, called out. "That ain't fair. You're suppose to die." The boy fired again.

"Oh!" Lance fell into play. Squeezing his eyes closed, he grabbed his stomach and doubled over. He stumbled toward the side of a building and collapsed against it.

Through a slitted gaze, he watched the little fellows' mouths drop open. Lance did not move.

Eyes wide with astonishment, they looked at the toy guns. After a few seconds they sidled cautiously up to him.

"Mister?" The redhead got brave. He looked back at his friend. "Ya think he's really dead?"

The first boy shrugged. "Shake him and see."

One finger extended, Carrot-top poked Lance.

Lance drew up to his full height. "Thought I was suppose to play dead."

Both boys nearly jumped out of their pants with a holler.

Lance grinned. Stumpy had done the same thing to him when he was a kid, and it had scared him, too. But all of that had changed now. He and his brothers were no longer kids. He looked at the two youngsters and lowered his voice. "You shouldn't ever point a gun—even a pretend one—at anyone. You could get hurt."

Chests heaving, the boys nodded. Then, without so much as a see-ya-later, they whirled away from Lance and raced out the opposite end of the alley. The devil himself could not have frightened them more.

Shaking his head with a smirk, he returned his thoughts to the saloon and Shea. He rounded the corner and started down the planked walk of Main Street.

Reno had become quite the bustling little town with shops of every imagining, banks, saloons. A hodgepodge of people from every corner of the world. There were two liveries, one near each end of town. Dance halls boasted of beautiful and exotic women performing outlandish feats, some public—most not.

He had been in too big of a hurry to notice much when he had arrived, but now his gaze could not seem to settle on any one thing for very long. There was so much to see. Even Chicago could not match this rip-roaring nugget of gold in the desert.

There were gambling houses aplenty advertising every kind of liquor known to man. Some even

Lance with his extensive travels had heard of but never tasted. Still more saloons. And everywhere people were spending money. Yeah. Reno might be small in size, but quite possibly it was the biggest, rowdiest little urban sprawl this side of the Great Divide.

Passing by a store, Lance caught his reflection in the glass. He hesitated. It never ceased to amaze him how strange it was to see the patch over his eye. Nor how different it made him look. Even now, after all of this time, it was as if he were seeing someone else. No wonder people stared. He did look like a robber.

A movement inside the shop caught his attention. He leaned closer to the glass and looked inside. An elderly woman with salt-and-pepper hair was scribbling on a tablet of paper.

Rearing back, Lance peered up at the lettering on the window. Madame Monique Rochette's Boutique, Fine Apparel for Ladies. Winter Magic flashed in his memory. For all of her good intentions of wanting to live like a white woman, how was it she had not yet discovered the necessity of ladies' undergarments? She could not just keep running around like she was. It was almost indecent, not to mention mighty uncomfortable for a man.

He lifted a brow. Should he? Would she be angry with such a personal gift from a man she barely knew? A ruckus from the bar at the end of the street drew his attention. He was supposed to be meeting Shea right now. He looked back at the store.

His gaze fell on the pale blue bathing costume displayed in the window case. He had not seen such a garment this far west, but back East they were quite the rage with all the ladies.

What were those lacy little undershirts called again? He squinted through the pane. None were in sight. Of course not. That would be too easy. This was ridiculous. How could he hope to make such a purchase if he did not know what to ask for? He certainly was not going to go inside and make a fool of himself over one.

Men did not have these problems. They had long johns—red or white—nothing more. Their only decision was whether to wear them or not. He suddenly felt like every male eye in town was watching him. He glanced around. What if someone saw him? A light tinkling sounded from the entrance.

"It is lovely, isn't it?" A lady's eloquent voice barely touched Lance's consciousness.

He turned to see a pretty blond woman clutching several paper-wrapped packages standing no more than a couple of feet from him. Unbound by the gray bonnet dangling at the back of her head, her pale crown of curls shimmered in the afternoon light.

Lance dipped his head. "Yes, ma'am." Touching the brim of his Stetson, he offered her a gracious smile. He felt more than a little self-conscious about being caught peeping through the window.

"Are you thinking of buying that for your wife?"

"Uh—no." Dismissing the word *wife*, Lance tried to envision the voluminous garment on Winter Magic. He scratched his temple. It just did not seem to fit the image of the Indian woman.

"Oh." She smiled brightly. "Then it must be for a sister . . . or a fiancée perhaps?"

Lance shook his head. Cutting his gaze to the blonde, he shifted his weight. Who was this woman? And why was she so curious? "I wasn't really looking for—"

The slightest shade of pink tinged her cheeks. "Oh, I am sorry. I didn't mean to pry. It's just, well, men don't usually stop to look in a ladies' store unless they're shopping for someone special."

Yeah. Winter Magic *was* that. He remembered how tantalizing she had looked earlier that morning when she had slipped on her blouse over her wet breasts. His stomach tightened. Maybe she did not need to be bound up by such a thing after all. Who said *all* the ways of the whites were best?

Damn. He shoved the lusty thoughts aside. What was wrong with him anyhow? Here he was standing in front of a beautiful woman who was going to great pains to make conversation with him, and all he could think about was Winter Magic.

Lance suddenly became aware of the lady's intense scrutiny. He felt as if *he* were the costume on display. The hairs on the back of his neck bristled. Damn it, but he was tired of being stared at all the time. He could admit that his features were a bit startling, but were they really that gruesome?

"Pardon me, sir."

He cut her an uncomfortable glare. Why the hell did she have to be so polite? Anger welled inside him. Why did everyone have to be so polite when all they really wanted to do was stomp a mudhole in his pain? He turned fully around to face her. If she wanted to gawk, he would give her the opportunity. "What is it?" He did not try to hide his annoyance.

"I couldn't help but notice—"

"What?" Cut the sweetness crap, lady.

She blinked, then much to his chagrin, flashed a condescending smile. "You wouldn't by any chance be Lance Taggert, would you?"

Surprised, Lance could only stare. He had not expected her to know him. He searched her face. To his recollection, they had not even seen each other before now. He furrowed his brow. "Yeah, I'm Lance Taggert."

The soft light in her blue eyes twinkled brighter. "I'd heard you were home. And there is the Taggert family resemblance." She offered him her hand. "I'm Gretchen Samuels—Dr. Garret Samuels's wife. My husband is a very close friend of your brother, Eldon."

Accepting her handshake, Lance lifted a relieved smile. "Garret Samuels? I don't believe I've had the pleasure just yet."

The woman arched a graceful brow. "You will. Eldon and Garret are virtually inseparable."

Lance held back a chuckle. If her husband had any of her refined and educated charm, Lance found that hard to believe. Eldon had never been known for his social graces.

Soft laughter escaped her. "You Taggert boys are quick, aren't you?"

"Pardon?" Lance frowned.

"I'm sorry." She flashed a row of even pearly teeth. "I mean, you can't have been home more than a day or two at most, and you're—" She gestured toward the shop window. "You were thinking of buying something in there, weren't you?"

Lance felt his face flame hot. This woman was as direct as Winter Magic.

"I'm sorry," she said again, turning almost as red as Lance felt. "It's really none of my business."

"It's quite all right."

The heavy clunk of approaching footsteps drew Lance's attention.

Coming up behind the woman, Shea grinned.

Gretchen Samuels turned and followed Lance's line of vision. "Shea." She dipped her head. "How nice to see you."

"Gretchen." Shea nodded.

"You don't seem to come into town as much as Eldon."

"No, ma'am. Now that winter's set in, I've been seein' to all the repairs that we didn't get to over the summer." Shea looked back at Lance. "I see you've met my other big brother."

"Yes. And I'm afraid I interrupted his shopping."

"Shoppin'?" Surprise marked Shea's features. He eyed the sign painted on the window of the lady's store, then squinted at Lance. "You were shoppin'? Here?"

Before Lance could answer, Gretchen Samuels cut in. "Oh, Shea. He wasn't inside. He was just looking through the window deciding whether or not he *should* go inside." She turned to Lance, an impish smile playing across her lips.

Lance cringed. Why was it that women always took such delight in embarrassing a man? Seeking to change the subject, he cleared his throat. "Did you find El?"

Shea nodded, his expression sobering. "I found him."

"Where?"

Instead of answering, he cut a glance to Gretchen Samuels before returning his gaze to Lance.

The woman must have realized that this conversation was not meant for her to hear. "Forgive me, gentlemen. I really must be about the rest of my business. I have to go out to the Run of the Red Deer Ranch, and I still have quite a few things to take care of before I can go."

"You seein' to Yitakam?"

Gretchen Samuels smiled, then arched a brow. "You don't have a problem with that, do you, Shea?" she asked, a note of sarcasm in her voice.

"Not me."

"Yitakam?" Lance interrupted. "Isn't that Tunupiuts's wife?"

"Yes." She answered Lance with the same intolerant tone she had used with Shea.

"How long before the baby comes?"

Lance's brows shot up. "Baby? Tunupiuts and Yitakam are expecting another baby?" Why had his old friend not mentioned this to him?

"She's very close to her time now."

"Well, I'll be damned."

Gretchen Samuels's eyes widened with Lance's last word.

"Excuse me, Mrs. Samuels, but Tunupiuts and I go back a long time, and I just saw him the other day, and well—he didn't say a word."

Gretchen Samuels's whole demeanor suddenly shifted. She took a deep breath and stiffened her back. "No, Mr. Taggert. He probably didn't. He's probably not sure just which side you're on yet."

"Side?" Lance darted a quizzical look between Shea and the woman.

"I really must be going. Shea. Mr. Taggert." That said, she walked away, more than an ample amount of rigidness in the gait of her step.

Frowning, Lance pulled a puzzled expression. "What did she mean by that?"

"I thought you knew about the hard feelin's between the Paiute Ranch and Eldon."

"Yeah."

"Well. That's what she's talkin' about." Shea wheeled around and started off in the opposite direction.

Lance caught up to him. "So she was insinuating that I might be taking El's side in all of this?"

"Gretchen doesn't *insinuate* anything. You get to know her better, and you'll find that out real quick. That's one woman that says exactly what she means."

Lance shot an understanding look over his shoulder. "I believe that." Halfway down the street, he nodded toward the saloon where the brothers were supposed to have met for a drink. "That where El is?"

"Yup."

"Good."

"You might not think so once you see him. El's well on his way to bein' liquored up, and he's with a bunch of his buddies."

Lance did not like the way Shea announced that El was with his friends. "What're you saying? You think we should just let what happened go?"

Shea shrugged. "I'm not tellin' you anythin' except that he's surrounded by his buddies."

As they approached the Gold Bug Saloon, Lance heard the pounding of ivory keys on a slightly out-of-tune piano. The voices from within grew steadily louder, but he could distinguish the words of one man over the garbled noise of the bar.

"I don't know why you're having such a problem with this, Eldon." The rich baritone of an obviously well-educated man rose even louder. "You've always told us what an Indian-lover Lance was."

"Yeah," another man shouted. "Once some men've had a taste of that wild and fiery Injun blood, they jist ain't satisfied with the sweetness of a white woman anymore."

Halting in front of the swinging doors leading into the saloon, Lance stiffened.

A chorus of hearty laughter rang out through the cavernous room. His gaze swept over the painted saloon girls garbed in vibrant-colored frocks who leaned indiscreetly against a patron here and there.

Jaws clenched, fists bunched, Lance scanned the crowd of faces for the man who had just spoken. He recognized several as hands from the Triple-T, but none stood out as the one who had just hurled the insult.

He targeted his older brother with a scowl. So. Eldon had discussed the morning's proceedings with his *buddies*, as Shea had put it, not to mention his past with Neme? Lance's blood ran hot.

"Did you really think he had changed?" The distinguished-looking man in a black suit and matching string tie stood next to Eldon. His very proper eastern accent and refined manner were in

complete contrast to his derogatory statement. He
nodded toward the crowd. "Although I question
his choice of words, Pete's right. Any white man
who takes an Indian for a wife isn't fit to be
accepted back into civilized society." He turned
toward the bar and finished under his breath. "Or
any woman, either."

Rage stormed inside of Lance. He studied each
face in turn, then came to rest on the poised man,
and finally on his older brother. Who the hell did
these men think they were to set themselves and
their standards above everyone else's? He looked
back at the man resting his elbows on the bar next
to Eldon. There was something cold and hard—
something akin to hatred, yet worse—lurking in the
glimmer of the man's stern eyes.

Without thought to his actions, Lance pushed
through the swinging doors.

The saloon became deafeningly silent.

Experience prompting his senses, Lance took in
the threat of his position. If there was to be a
confrontation, which after his entrance there un-
doubtedly would be, he had best foresee all advan-
tages.

Eldon stiffened. His dark stare sharpened, and
his right hand lowered within inches of his holster.

The man in the suit shot a questioning glance at
Eldon before returning his gaze to Lance, a look of
realization marking his features. A slow smile
curled his mouth. Withdrawing from the bar, he
extended a hand past Eldon. "You must be Lance.
I'm Garret Samuels—Doc to my friends."

Training a fixed glare on Eldon,, Lance ignored
the proffered greeting. He heard Shea move up

behind him. "We have some things we need to talk about, El."

"*We* don't got nothin' to talk about."

Lance kept his eye pinned on Eldon, his other senses wary of the rest of the men in the room. *This* was one of the exact reasons he had left the governor's agency. With only one eye he could not hope to see everyone and watch their movements. His vision was too limited.

Reaching for a shot glass, Samuels filled it full of whiskey, then held it out to Lance. He darted an amused look between the brothers. "Why don't you have a drink with us?"

"Stay out of this, Samuels."

The doctor's brows shot upward.

Lance had no intention of even pretending to be friendly with the doctor. He did not like him, nor did he trust the man's motives. "Look, I don't care who you are, but I'd like to talk to my brother— without interference from any of you." The latter he directed to the throng of men that had moved a little closer.

Shea stepped nearer. "This might not be such a good time," he said, keeping his voice low. "There's too many of 'em."

His younger brother was right. The two of them could not hold these men off should there be a fight. He was at too much of a disadvantage. He started to back down, but noticing the smirk growing on Eldon's face, he suddenly could not. He had to stand his ground, yet he would have to keep things under control. He did not budge from his position.

Eldon had started something back at the hot

springs, and by God, Lance was determined to see it finished. He counted the men surrounding him. The odds were against him ten to one.

How many times in the past had he found himself in a similar situation? Too many. But he had had the full use of his eyesight then. He had to trim the odds down to his favor. "Let's go someplace where we can talk in private, El."

"I like it right here. Besides, I think you said all I needed to hear back there with your squaw."

Every muscle in Lance's body went taut.

"Eldon. Relax." Garret Samuels set down the glass of whiskey. He turned to face them. With a glance toward the crowd, he flashed Lance a meaningful smile. "I'm quite certain your brother doesn't want to start anything in here. Why don't you listen to what he's got to say?"

Sharpening his glare, Lance shot Samuels a look of warning. "I don't need any help from you."

"Excuse me." The doctor lifted his hands apologetically. "I was merely trying to make things easier."

Shea snorted. "In a mule's ass."

Instantly the bodies around them went rigid.

Eldon's hand moved closer to the gun strapped to his leg. "You two ain't got that squaw bitch here to protect you now."

A low rumble of chuckles filtered up through the thick air.

Lance felt the hairs on his arms stand on end. "Leave Winter Magic out of this. This's been coming on between us for a long time."

"Winter Magic!" Eldon spat on the planked floor. "You just couldn't stand it, could you? You ain't been home two days good, and you're already trying to replace that first Injun bitch of yours with another one.''

Was Eldon right? He had not taken another Indian woman to his bed since Neme. Why had he tried now? A mixture of guilt and anger coursed through Lance. Why *had* his lust been incited so fast with Winter Magic? He could not think straight. Nor could he hold back his temper. He had to retaliate. ''You think I'm horning in on your territory or something?''

''What's that supposed to mean?'' Eldon flicked a nervous glare between Lance and his friend at the bar.

''What? Don't all your *buddies* here know about your Indian women?''

''Shut your mouth!''

''Don't.'' Shea nudged him. ''You don't know what you're doin'.''

Lance knew he should listen to his younger brother. These men clearly thought anyone who associated himself with Indians was of the lowest breed. But he could not stop. ''Do they know about Tuhu'—your—''

''Lance!'' Shea grabbed his upper arm and pulled. Their gazes clashed. ''You don't want to do this.''

''The hell I don't! He started this, now I'm going to finish it.'' Lance did not mean to sound so harsh. He knew Shea only wanted to get him out of there with his skin, but Eldon had pushed him too far. ''You can leave if you want.''

''Yeah, Shea. Leave,'' Eldon commanded.

Lance felt the tautness in Shea's grip flex.

The younger man's hand slipped down to his side.

"Back off, Shea," Lance warned in a throaty whisper. He could feel his brother's anger mount. "This's between Eldon and me."

After another moment of pressing silence, Shea relaxed his stance. He nodded. "Okay, Lance. It's your show." He stepped back a pace.

Eldon squared off in front of Lance. His eyes narrowed. He unsnapped his Colt, then poised an open palm above his gun butt.

The crowd moved back, enlarging the circle around the vying men.

Lance probed Eldon with a penetrating stare. His stomach clenched tighter. What the hell were they doing? Could he shoot his own brother? And for what? Winter Magic's reputation? No. The stake wedged between him and Eldon went deeper than that. Still. What did he have to prove here? That he was a man?

"You gonna draw that leg iron?" Eldon narrowed his gaze.

Lance's jaw nearly popped with rage. His teeth ground into each other so hard he was sure everyone could hear the noise.

Eldon eyed him long and hard. He appeared to be contemplating Lance's position. "You gone yella?"

Every muscle in Lance's body snapped tight against his bones. Why was Eldon pushing him into a fight? He could not draw down on his own brother. "We don't need to do this, El. Let's talk."

"Talk, hell! I'd rather eat dirt!" He cut Lance a

sidled look. "What's wrong? You need yourself a
Injun gal to watch before you can stiffen that
backbone of yours and act like a man?"

Lance's anger returned. "Hold it right there—"

Disregarding his brother, Eldon tossed a glance
into the crowd. "Where's Princess?"

"Here!" someone yelled.

Through the throng of jeering faces, a young and
obviously frightened girl of maybe sixteen or seventeen was shoved toward Eldon. Garbed in a
buckskin dress with gaudy beadwork and a flour-
ish of bright feathers in her braided hair, the girl
appeared less than noble in her demeanor.

Eldon grabbed her wrist and yanked her to him.
"This is Princess. See this?" He pinched her jaws
between his thumb and fingers, twisting her face
toward Lance. "This here's the mark of the dirty
nose. You know what that means, don't you?"

Lance grimaced at the small crescent scar marring
her otherwise innocent features.

"She's Bannock, and they don't take kindly to
their women beddin' down a man before they've
gotten their price outta her on a good trade." He
planted a noisy kiss square on her mouth. "Why,
Princess here is just what you're lookin' for. Young,
and except for that nose, she ain't half bad to look
at, either—a Injun bitch in heat and ready for the
takin'."

With terrified eyes she struggled but could not
break Eldon's grasp.

He raised a brow and smiled. "You want her?"

Anyone could see the girl was no more than a
child.

Lance had to stop him. His eyes burned hot. He took a step forward and drew back a fist. Pain splintered his head. Stars stung his eyes. He crumpled to the floor. Then all went black.

9

Winter Magic sat alone inside her family's roundhouse staring up at the many layers of its cedar-bark roof. She sighed. When they had broken off from the main tribe to start a new life here in the valley, she had tried to convince her uncle to build a ranch house like the whites, but he would not be swayed.

"Some things need to remain familiar," she remembered Nighthawk saying. *"Our group will need to still feel a part of the tribe. A few of the old ways will not hold us back. It will be easier to move them into the new if we first allow them the security of what they know."*

Nighthawk was a wise man. He had been one of the most respected headmen of the Coo-yu-ee Pah Paiutes since he was a young brave. Solely by reputation he had convinced the people to listen to Winter Magic's plan for their own ranch.

Her gaze traced the strands of fiber hanging from

a cedar limb which made up their sacred Bear Dance Flag. It was a great honor to house this symbol.

Pride swelled within her and she smiled to herself. Once, not so long ago, the Paiutes had been a strong, powerful, and respected nation. Soon they would be again. She nodded as if someone were there with her. Truly Nighthawk *was* very wise. A little of the old mixed in with the new served to remind all of their noble heritage, as well as guide them to a bountiful future. If only they could make friends with the whites—gain their respect—work and live beside them.

Again, Winter Magic sighed. She picked up a discarded flute made of arrowcane and rolled it absently between her palms. She hoped she had not lost, through the ordeal with the Ganoida bui, what small amount of status she had obtained since the incident with Owl Eyes.

Since she had returned home the day before, she had hardly spoken to anyone save her aunt. Her uncle was in the sweathouse, where he had been for two days with the elders, praying for the birth of a healthy son.

Would he shun her from her people? She had prayed to the Great Spirit as he had instructed. She had received the message from the god. Maybe if she could convince Nighthawk that Lance Taggert had been sent to this valley by the Great Spirit, he would not punish her further.

But what to say to her uncle? The Ganoida bui had sounded as though he did not wish to see the valley torn apart. He appeared genuinely concerned and not fond of Eldon Taggert's methods.

Surely he would help her people—he must. The Great Spirit had sent him.

And what of her? Would her uncle read her enthusiasm about the Ganoida bui as something else? Was it more than enthusiasm? She was so confused. Why had she allowed herself to almost make love with him? She barely knew him. Had she truly found him too attractive to resist? She shuddered at the answer to her wanton question. Yes.

Still, it was much more than his looks. He had a hint of loneliness about him—a touch of sadness that drew her to him. How well Winter Magic understood those emotions. True, she had her uncle and his family, but they were not her parents. And since Owl Eyes, she had not permitted herself the closeness of another brave. Never again would *she* be the cause for the tribe to banish one of their members.

Why *had* the people driven him away? Was what the two of them had done truly so terrible? At seventeen summers Owl Eyes was considered a man. Why had he and Winter Magic not been allowed to marry? Other maidens had been taken as wives by the age of thirteen.

But other maidens had not been caught lying with a suitor who had not been approved by the family. Not that others had not indulged in such acts—they simply had not been caught.

Even now, nine years later, the people had not forgotten her sin. After receiving a severe beating by the women, she had been allowed to remain among them, but with a loss in status. And only after enduring the constant bantering of harsh words with her head held high, not to mention hard work, did she finally manage to elevate her standing within the small group of her tribesmen at the ranch. But still, no men of the tribe ever came to ask Nighthawk for Winter Magic.

She squeezed her eyes closed against the sudden sting of tears. Silently she said a small prayer of thanks to the gods for her uncle and aunt's love and affection. In the openness of the tribe, Nighthawk had to abide by her punishment, though after the beating, he did not allow anyone to harm her. But in the seclusion of their own roundhouse, he and her aunt took her to their hearts and gave her the strength she needed to bear the torment. Having no girl children themselves, they had loved her as their own.

The hide covering the door whipped aside, and someone poked a head through the opening.

Winter Magic blinked back the tears and sniffled. With a quick swipe she brushed the moisture from her cheeks. Straining her vision, the limited firelight allowed her to make out only a silhouette against the glare of the winter day outside.

"Am I disturbing you?"

Winter Magic smiled. She would know the voice of Moon Dove anywhere. "*Kai.*" She motioned for her to enter, then held up her arms and embraced her friend. Releasing the white woman, she offered her a place beside her in front of the fire.

Sitting down, Moon Dove set Dr. Samuels's black leather bag on the ground next to her. She had brought some of her husband's medicines.

Winter Magic mentally shook her head. How could a woman as loving as Gretchen Samuels be married to such a hateful man? She extended the buffalo robe that draped her lap across her friend's.

"Yitakam tells me you're waiting to speak to Tunupiuts."

Winter Magic nodded. "My aunt tells you true." Without thought she retrieved a comb from a rabbit-fur pouch and began untangling her hair. Her gaze shifted to the dancing flames warming the interior. "What else did Yitakam tell you?" She swallowed nervously. She, herself, had spoken to her friend of the incident at the first meeting of the Ganoida bui, but to no one else. Had Nighthawk returned to tell of her shocking display in front of the man? Had she ruined her standing with the tribe? She had to know.

"Is there something else you should've told me?"

"No more than what I confessed when last we spoke." She lowered her head. She had brought the shame onto herself. She would have to accept the outcome.

"You mean about your run-in with Lance Taggert?"

Winter Magic nodded.

"No, Tu'madai. She said nothing."

A soft sigh of relief fluttered out from Winter Magic. She had prayed for her uncle's silence, hoped for it. And even though she knew how much he loved her, she had not expected it. After all, he was one of the headmen. He had his duty to the tribe. This small gift would not be forgotten. She would be forever grateful.

After a long moment of quiet, Moon Dove spoke. "Are you sure you wouldn't rather be alone?"

"*Kai*, please stay." Without looking up, Winter

Magic reached out and found her friend's hand. "You always seem to know when I need you."

The affectionate woman squeezed Winter Magic's fingers. "Friends are always there for each other. Here." She took the comb. "Let me do this."

Wanting to take her mind off her own worries, Winter Magic grasped another subject. "How does my aunt's labor progress?"

"Well enough for a woman of her years. And she's healthy. But since the last child was stillborn, I want to keep a close watch on her."

"But it goes so slow and she looks to be in much pain." Winter Magic envisioned her pregnancy-swollen aunt trudging around the small group of roundhouses, a party of women-elders at her heels. Every so often a stab of pain would cause Yitakam to grab the underside of her belly and her face would grow taut. "It makes me want to cry for her."

Gliding the comb through a thick lock of hair, Moon Dove smoothed the black cascade away from Winter Magic's face. She began braiding the mass into one long plait. "Is that why you were crying when I came in—because of your aunt?"

Winter Magic held herself to silence. She closed her eyes and tried to relax under the gentle ministrations of her friend. If ever she could confide in anyone, Moon Dove was that person. But dare she confess what she had done with Ganoida bui at the hot springs? No. She could not have the woman believing her to be shameless.

"There. How's that?" Moon Dove must have sensed her friend's reluctance to answer, and so did not press her further.

Opening her eyes, Winter Magic glanced down at the long braid draping her shoulder. Halfway to her waist, the intricate weave was tied off with a shiny yellow ribbon. She lifted the unbound portion of her hair, then fingered the smooth texture of the thin sash. A rush of happiness flooded her body. She turned to stare at her friend. "Is this for me?"

Moon Dove smiled. "Do you like it?"

"Oh, *pisha'*." She reached out and gave the woman a heartfelt hug. "It is most beautiful."

"I saw it in a little store in Reno yesterday while I was shopping for your aunt and the baby." Her eyes sparkled as she spoke. "I just knew this color would be lovely tied in your black hair."

"Thank you, Muha ihovi. It is a wonderful gift." Leaning back, she touched the satiny strands. A present was just what she had needed to lift her spirits. "But I have no gift for you."

"Tu'madai." The white woman patted her hand. "I didn't give you that so you'd give me something in return. I bought it for you because I thought you would like it."

"Oh, *pisha'*, I do—very much."

"Good. Here now." She reached out and gathered the braid again. "You've untied it. Let me fix it for you."

Scooting closer, Winter Magic smiled. It had been a long time since anyone had given her such a wonderful present. And for a few seconds she forgot her fretfulness.

"Guess who I met yesterday?"

Winter Magic blinked. Strange question. She had no idea who Moon Dove could be talking about.

"I met Mr. Taggert."

Puzzled, Winter Magic frowned.

"Lance. Your Ganoida bui." Moon Dove grinned. "I can see why you gave him that name, too. He's a very handsome man. And he certainly didn't waste any time managing to make himself popular with the ladies."

"What does this mean?" She had an idea she knew exactly what it meant. And she did not like it. "Have you seen him with a woman?"

"Well, no." She raised her brows questioningly. "Why?"

A lump lodged in Winter Magic's throat. She had been deceived. That was not loneliness she had seen in Lance Taggert, but lust. She clenched her teeth and dug her nails into the palms of her hands. "It is just a curious thing. Do you not agree?"

Moon Dove shrugged. "Only that *you* find it curious." She studied Winter Magic a long moment before continuing. "I was only joking. I did catch him peeking in Madame Rochette's—"

"Madame Rochette's?" Who was this woman and why had the Ganoida bui been watching her?

"It's a ladies' shop. He was looking at a swimming costume that was on display in the window."

"They make clothing for swimming?" Some of the white customs were just a little too strange for her to imagine. "How silly. Who would want to wear such a thing? The whole purpose for going into the water is to clean yourself."

"Yes, well, not always. Sometimes people go into the water to play and refresh themselves."

"Did Lance Taggert buy this swimming clothes?"

"No. But when I teased him about making such a purchase for a lady friend, he didn't deny it." She twisted her face into an aloof expression. "It may be presumptuous of me, but since he hasn't been back long enough to acquaint himself with any of the town's respectable ladies, that only leaves the girls at Maudy Beth's."

"But he did not buy it?" Winter Magic's question sounded more like a statement. She had no wish to believe Lance Taggert was a man with insatiable appetites and had chosen to consort with soiled women. Nor that their indiscretion had simply happened because of the man's overpowering need, and she being the only female available at the moment.

Moon Dove shook her head. Her gaze rushed past Winter Magic's defenses. "I don't think I've ever known you to be so concerned for any man before. Why this Lance Taggert? I thought you hated him."

"I don't hate anyone—except maybe his brother, Eldon." And your husband, she thought silently. Since Moon Dove's capture and return from the Bannock, there had been no love between her friend and the doctor. The couple lived in the same house, but no more. She was sure of it. She did not know why. She had never asked. It was not her place.

And she would not tell her friend of the many disturbing flashes of hate and lust that Garret Samuels had branded on her skin. It had repulsed her. It was as if he blamed her and all other Indians for what had happened to his wife. But she would not hurt Moon Dove with this knowledge.

"So why do you find Lance so *curious*?"

Winter Magic snapped out of her thoughts. "Who?"

"Your Ganoida bui." Moon Dove arched a brow.

Winter Magic glanced at the fire. "I believe him to be pure of heart."

"I'm afraid I don't understand."

Looking back at her friend, Winter Magic hesitated. Should she tell her that her prayers had been answered? She took a deep breath. "He was sent to us by the Great Spirit."

The blond woman pulled a frown. "Sent?"

Nodding, Winter Magic smiled. "The Great Spirit has sent us a warrior to end this fight between our two peoples here in the valley."

Moon Dove grimaced. "Really? And the Great Spirit told you this?"

"He did not actually tell me, *kai*. I asked him for a sign, and the Ganoida bui rode into my camp."

"He was with you while you were praying?" Moon Dove's voice pitched, a mask of disapproval marking her features. "Does Tunupiuts know he was there?"

"*Kai*," she answered a bit too quickly. Cutting her gaze away from Moon Dove's probing stare, she shook her head. "That is why I wish to speak to him."

"What happened to cause you to need to speak with your uncle?" Her friend leaned nearer. "Look at me."

Obeying the woman, she lifted shame-filled eyes.

"Oh, my God," Moon Dove whispered. "You didn't let him—"

"*Kai*!" Again she answered too quickly.

"But he tried, didn't he?" She grabbed Winter Magic's hands. Angry words spewed from her mouth. "The bastard tried. By all means, you need to tell Tunupiuts. Damn those Taggerts. The only one with any morals is Shea—and I'm not completely convinced he's not just as big a monster as his brothers. Their kind have no respect for Indians—especially for the women."

"You don't understand—"

"It's *you* who doesn't understand. It's beyond me why you want your people to merge into the white man's world. And they call you heathens. Hmph!" Moon Dove's body tensed. Her eyes took on a savage light. "They're no better than heathens themselves. Your men are hard on a woman, but they have a gentle side, too. One that's capable of laughter, warmth, and love—"

"It did not happen the way you think." Winter Magic shook her friend. She had to calm her. She understood how Dr. Samuels had treated his wife after the woman's return from the Bannocks', but Winter Magic could not have her believing that Lance Taggert was like him.

Moon Dove's eyes rounded. "How *did* it happen?" she asked in a softer tone.

Hesitating, Winter Magic pooled her thoughts. "What you believe to have taken place between me and Ganoida bui did not." A moment of quiet skittered across her nerves.

The two women sat staring at each other, neither speaking. But in that single moment of silence Winter Magic realized her heart had shone through her eyes, and she had already revealed too much.

"But you wanted it to . . . didn't you?" Moon Dove's voice was no longer filled with harshness.

Winter Magic shrugged. "I cannot say for certain. My mind said no, but when he touched my

lips . . ." Of their own volition her fingers brushed
her mouth. "My body would not listen."

"Oh, my good Lord. You're smitten with the
man. He's barely been home a day, two at most, and
he's already—" Shaking her head, she broke off.
"Isn't Lance supposed to be a good friend of
Tunupiuts?"

"*Pisha'*."

Moon Dove rolled her eyes, then looked back at
Winter Magic. "What in heaven's name were you
two thinking of?" But before Winter Magic could
defend their actions, Moon Dove raised her hand.
"You're letting your emotions lead you astray. The
Great Spirit didn't send Lance Taggert. More than
likely, Eldon did."

Winter Magic scowled. "Why would he do that?'

Standing, Moon Dove began to pace. "To try to
win you to their side. If Lance had managed to
compromise you, they could blackmail you into
submission—to make you convince Tunupiuts of
the futility of the Run of the Red Deer Ranch."

"Blackmail? Futility?" Winter Magic did not understand these words.

Moon Dove nodded. "They know what would
happen to a Paiute woman should her people find
out that a white man had taken her to his bed. The
law is still the same."

Winter Magic remembered the last women who
had suffered the proscribed punishment. The memory of burning flesh touched her nostrils, the
woman's screams pierced her hearing . . . She
shuddered. She had no wish to suffer the same fate.
She leapt to her feet, tears threatening. "Nothing

happened. You must believe me. I speak the truth. The Ganoida bui is a good man. He has no wish to see the valley torn apart. I believe he truly cares for us."

"What makes you say that?"

Winter Magic thought for a minute. What had he actually said or done to convince her of that? Nothing really. Still . . . "It is something in the way that he talks to me whenever he speaks of this valley and the people who live here. He does not wish to see blood spilled."

Moon Dove smiled. "You're still so young. You truly believe that, don't you?"

"He has given me no reason to think otherwise."

"He only wants what's best for his family. He doesn't care about your people's ranch. Other than just being childhood friends with Tunupiuts, why would he? He probably has about as much love for Indians as—" Moon Dove paused. "As his brother."

"*Kai.* He took an Indian for a wife."

Moon Dove's eyes widened. "Lance is married?" She shook her head as if she did not trust her friend. "He didn't say that when I asked him yesterday. Where—who is she?"

"I believe her name was Neme—"

Moon Dove's hand flew to her mouth. She cut a nervous glance toward the flap covering the opening to the roundhouse. "Wasn't she a member of your tribe? The one that—"

"*Pisha'.*"

"Does he know what happened to her?"

"I cannot say for certain. I believe he does."

"And you still think he *cares* for your people?" Moon Dove asked, disbelief tingeing her tone.

Winter Magic had never been angry with her friend, but now, in the defense of the Ganoida bui, she found her temper mounting. "You do not know him."

"Neither do you."

The animal hide covering the entrance flopped open, and Nighthawk came into view. "Muha ihovi."

Winter Magic flinched. Had he heard them arguing?

"The time for the child is here. Yitakam waits for you with the other women."

"*Pisha'*." Moon Dove bowed her head respectfully. She cut her friend one last look—one that Winter Magic could not fully read.

Crossing the hide and fur-covered floor, she bent down next to where Winter Magic stood and retrieved the leather bag she had brought in with her. "Sometimes a minimum of truth is best," she whispered.

Winter Magic frowned. Their eyes met.

Moon Dove gestured toward Nighthawk with a sidelong glance.

Though Winter Magic was not completely certain what her friend meant by a *minimum of truth*, she knew the statement offered her was one made out of genuine concern.

"The little one comes," Nighthawk announced more harshly than Winter Magic had ever heard him speak to Moon Dove. It was painfully obvious he could not hide the tension brought on by the impending birth of his third child. His features softened, as did his eyes when he looked upon the white woman again. "Yitakam calls for you. You will go to her now?"

"*Pisha'*, Tunupiuts." She smiled in her gentle, reassuring way that had always told Winter Magic all would be well. "I will go."

After Moon Dove's departure, her uncle remained in the roundhouse with Winter Magic. He took a seat near the fire, then signaled her to join him. "Sit with me. I would have you talk to me while I wait for my new son."

She swallowed. She had anticipated this moment since she had returned. She must make her uncle see Lance Taggert as the sign the Great Spirit had delivered to her through her prayers. Even though she knew the Ganoida bui to be an old friend of Nighthawk's, she was not certain her uncle would accept the man as being the warrior sent to end the battle between her people and the Triple-T. The man was white, not to mention a Taggert.

Nighthawk cleared his throat.

She darted him a wary gaze.

He secured the antelope-skin robe tied at his throat closer to his body. A sheen of perspiration brought on from the hours spent in the sweathouse still covered his face and chest. "Moon Dove sounded angry."

She had hoped her uncle had not noticed. Winter Magic's stomach tightened.

"Who were you talking about?" He appeared determined.

"Who?"

Nighthawk nodded. "She is an uncommon white. I have never known her to walk in anger." His dark-eyed gaze pierced her soul. "I would learn what troubles her. Who is this person you do not know well . . . and why does this worry Muha ihovi?"

⚊10⚊

Winter Magic studied the questioning creases in her uncle's forehead. Would he believe her story? And if he did not, what then would she do? If her uncle did not agree, should she go against the Great Spirit and follow Nighthawk's wishes? To defy either would go against her teachings.

She bit her lower lip. She was making this worse by trying to second-guess the outcome.

"Komeni Tu'madai?"

At the sound of her name she blinked.

"Did you hear the question?"

"*Pisha'*."

"Will you not answer?"

"I will answer, Uncle. I hope you will listen." She took a deep breath and began. As she proceeded to tell Nighthawk of the circumstances surrounding her prayer, she watched his posture for any sign of disapproval.

But he remained ever attentive to the details, yet completely silent. Even when she told of the intrusion by the Ganoida bui's brothers.

Moon Dove's last words flashed uppermost in her thoughts. She suddenly understood the white woman's meaning and carefully omitted all *unnecessary* details.

"Is that all?" Nighthawk asked when she had finished.

She swallowed. *"Pisha'."* She did not like lying. It was not a habit she valued.

"Have you spoken to Lance Taggert of your message from the Great Spirit?"

"Kai. With all that took place at the hot springs, there was not time."

Nighthawk sat staring into the fire for a long moment.

The silence between them stretched so tight, Winter Magic thought she would surely scream with the strain of it. Watching him, she fought to endure. It would not be proper for her to interrupt his thoughts.

Finally he cleared his throat. "If what you tell me is true—" He paused.

Winter Magic held her breath.

"I believe it is a good and just sign. I have always known Lance Taggert to be a man with an honorable heart. He must be told. I do not think it wise for him to be allowed to walk blind among our hopes."

Winter Magic's heart picked up its tempo. Nighthawk believed her—better still, he approved. She could not have asked for more.

Nighthawk nodded as was his habit. "He must know that he is the warrior the Great Spirit has chosen."

"But, Uncle?" A stab of worry cut into her. "What if this does not please him? What if he does not choose to follow the path the Great Spirit has set him upon? What then?"

Nighthawk raised his brows. He did not answer right away. "It is a question worth asking. I will think on it while you are away."

Puzzled, Winter Magic stared at him. "Where am I going, Uncle?" Her breath caught, and her heart constricted against her chest. Did he somehow know of the brief intimacy she and the Ganoida bui had shared? Was he sending her away after all?

"You were the one given the sign, Komeni Tu-'madai. *You* must be the one to go and speak to Lance Taggert. Tell him all that the Great Spirit has revealed to you. I believe he will listen."

Relief flooded Winter Magic's being. He did not know. What was more, he was sending her to talk to the Ganoida bui herself. Pride swelling within her, she straightened her posture. This was a great honor. And, she had to admit, knowing she would soon see the white man again gave her more than a small amount of pleasure.

Nighthawk rose, then straightened his robe. "Yi-takam will bear my new son soon. It would bring me great joy to share my happiness with my friend, Lance Taggert." He turned as if to leave, but hesitated. He glanced over his shoulder. "Tell my brother of the birth. Ask him to come. We will celebrate the first of many to be born into this new life we have started here. I will send for the rest of our tribe. I would ask him to stand with me when I present the child to our people."

Winter Magic nodded. Her pulse hammered as she watched Nighthawk disappear through the opening and the hide fall back into place. Quickly she began to gather some supplies. Reaching for her coat, she flinched. A sudden barb pricked her mind. How was she going to get to the Ganoida bui? She would never be allowed to enter upon Triple-T soil.

She shook off the thought. After rolling up her provisions within a heavy bearskin robe, she raced outside. She would just have to find a way to overcome that obstacle when she got to the white ranch. But for now she only knew she was going to see Lance Taggert. And for now . . . it was enough.

Lance could feel the dull ache in the back of his head even before he opened his eyes. He cringed. His lids flew wide. He bolted upright, but the pain held him at bay. He groaned. Where was he? He lifted his head, caution marking his movements.

The hotel room that Shea had rented for them slowly came into focus. How had he gotten here? The last he remembered, he was about to punch—

Mid-thought, his gaze came to rest on a man slumped forward straddling a high-backed chair. He squinted. Now he recalled. Someone in the saloon had hit him from behind. His stare narrowed on the familiar form dozing in front of him. Shea. It had to have been him.

His earlier anger returned. Rising from the bed to a sitting position, he scowled at his brother. He kicked the front legs of the chair.

Shea toppled to the floor with a grunt. "What the—" Alarm creasing his features, he grabbed for his gun. His startled stare flew to Lance.

"You hit me?" Even as he asked the question, he knew the answer. Rubbing the back of his neck, he glared at Shea.

Cautiously the younger man stood. He picked up the chair and replaced it upright, his gaze never leaving Lance. "Couldn't see any other way outta there." He shrugged. "I tried to shut you up, but you wouldn't listen."

"So you hit me?"

"What the hell did you expect? No way could the two of us whip that bunch. And after what you said to El—"

"El? What about what he said to me?" Lance ripped off the patch from his eye. He crossed the room to the pitcher on the washstand, then poured a generous amount of water into the bowl. Did Shea care how Lance felt? "You saw what he did to that little Indian girl?"

Shea's expression remained passive.

Disgust welled up inside of Lance. "I guess you think that was okay, too?"

"I never said that."

"Yeah, and you didn't try to stop it, neither." After pulling off his shirt, Lance turned his back on the man and shook his head. "Maybe you didn't grow up with as much backbone as I thought."

"What's that s'pose to mean?" Shea's voice pitched low.

Lance tossed his shirt onto the bed, then splashed his face, letting the cool water soothe his throbbing head. He grabbed the towel hanging on the commode hook, dabbed his face, then turned toward the stern expression of his brother.

"It means," Lance hurled the terrycloth against the oval mirror above the washbowl, "I can't believe you'd side with El. I thought I'd pegged you right. But I see now. You just don't give a damn about anyone, do you?"

Shea's jaw muscle twitched. "You don't know what you're talkin' about."

"Don't I?" Lance stiffened. He glowered at Shea, the blurred vision of his left eye putting a strain on his right. "I could've used your help in that damn saloon, but instead you do this." He made a hammering motion against the back of his neck.

"Hell, Lance, if I hadn't hit you, somebody else would've. I tried to tell you to keep quiet about Tuhu' and his mother, but you just kept on."

"Why the hell not? What makes El so privileged? From what I heard, he didn't even marry the boy's mother. You can have your fun with heathens, but for God's sakes don't marry them! Is that it?" He did not wait for Shea to answer. "You heard what he said about Neme. Hell, he even brought Winter Magic in on it."

"Yup, I heard." He peered at Lance with a knowing look. "And I saw, too."

"What?"

"You didn't get really mad till he brought up Winter Magic."

Lance's temper soared. Just what was Shea insinuating? "Hell, man. She saved our skins."

"Yup. She did that."

Lance flung his arms out. "So he can say anything he likes, but I can't?"

Shea paused. He wore a look of disbelief. "You gotta know that was the liquor talkin'. He was just mad."

"The hell I do." Lance strode across the room and picked up his traveling bag. He moved to the bed and slammed the case hard atop the mattress. "He's had it out for me from the first day in the barn. The liquor just made it worse."

Shea took a seat in the chair. "Longer than that."

Lance frowned at his brother's statement. After flinging open the satchel, he shot a questioning look over his shoulder.

Trancelike, Shea appeared to be in deep thought. "El's always been jealous of you. He admired you above all people, but he was jealous just the same."

"What do you mean?"

"He never had your strength. You went against Pa for Neme. You married her and started your own family. You didn't need Pa's approval, or the Triple-T. You saw what you wanted and went for it." He sharpened his gaze, focusing on Lance. "Even after you knew she was dead, you still didn't ask the old man for anything."

"Why should I?" Lance took a clean shirt from his bag and snapped it loose. "Pa's the one who sent her to die."

Pulling his mouth to one side, Shea nodded. "But then, it was Tunupiut's people who killed her." He quirked a brow. "Why don't you hold them responsible for any of this?"

Lance blinked. He had never been approached with that question before. Since his arrival, he had been reminded of Neme's death more times in the two days he had been home than the entire ten years he had been gone. He had managed to tuck his grief neatly away without too much torment. Why now was it resurfacing to haunt his every moment?

Shea did not speak, but his hazel eyes remained fixed on Lance.

Damn. The younger man had the patience of Job. And he obviously wanted an answer.

But what was Lance to say? He was not really sure himself why he had never directed his anger toward the Paiutes. Slipping on his shirt, Lance sat on the edge of the bed. "I never thought about it. I guess I just figured that was their way—their law."

"And you just accepted them puttin' her to death as just?" Shea sounded skeptical.

Lance found himself feeling as doubting as Shea looked. He nodded. For whatever reason, at the time he had not held the Paiutes accountable. He had been angry—no—as Stumpy might put it—*mad dog* pissed. But he had directed all of his hostility toward his father.

"So what makes Tunupiuts and his people so much better than Pa?"

Lance glared at Shea. "I don't think I follow you."

"Pa was only going by *his laws*. He didn't abide by Indians, and he didn't want his son to, neither."

"So you're saying 'cause *he* didn't like Indians and didn't want one for a daughter, him lying to Neme and sending her home to face that kind of punishment was okay?" It was a question he did not expect Shea to answer, but he was too angry to think about it.

"Was it okay for the old Paiute shaman to burn his own daughter at the stake? Just because she had chosen to marry a white man?" Shea leaned back and folded his arms over his chest. "I'm sorry, Lance, but I don't see a difference."

Lance stared at his younger brother. Suddenly he could not see a difference, either. Yet his pain and pride would not relent. "The Paiutes have lived by their laws down through the ages. Neme and I both knew how her people felt. We stayed clear of them, and they left us alone. If Pa had done the same, she'd be alive now."

"Pa didn't force her to go back to them—"

"No—not physically. He only told her I didn't love her—had *never* loved her. She didn't have anywhere else to go."

"Why didn't she just wait and find out from you for herself?"

"Who knows?" Lance yelled. Rage soared within him. The remembered pain of returning home to bitter lies and the torment of an empty home and two senseless deaths was more than he could hide. "He must've convinced her she needed to go home for the baby's sake."

Shea flinched.

"But what good did that do?" Lance railed. He was so caught up in his own grief, he could not think clearly. He lost control. His pent-up anger spewed out of his body. "She sacrificed herself for nothing. The poor little thing died just a week after she did."

Tears scalded his eyes. He blinked them back. "Damn it!" He jumped up and swiped the moisture from his face. Turning his back on his brother, he closed his eyes and took a few deep breaths.

"I—I'm sorry, Lance."

"Damn you, Shea," Lance murmured. "Damn you for bringing this all out again." He snatched his patch up from the bed, then still holding it, he buttoned his shirt. Silently, careful to avoid eye contact with Shea, he moved to the washstand. Nothing made any sense anymore. But why should it? He had never really faced any of it—his father's hatred, Neme's death, the loss of their baby girl—none of it. He had simply fled the pain.

Looking at his reflection, he started to put on his eyepatch, but stopped. He chuckled without mirth. "Funny."

"Beg pardon?"

"No matter how far or long you run, when you get back, your trouble's always waiting for you, isn't it?" He stared at the lighter shade of his injured eye. "Nothing ever just goes away."

"I guess not."

Lance caught Shea's troubled expression in the mirror.

"I'm really sorry. I didn't mean to make you—"

"It's okay." Lance took another cleansing breath. "I guess it had to come out sometime."

"You still mad?" Shea sounded almost childlike.

"Yeah." Lance looked back at himself. "But not at you."

"El?"

Hesitating, Lance released a resigned sigh. He shook his head. He tied on the patch, then secured it so that the small scars above and below his left eye were the only visible remains of his injury. He thought of Drew Jordan—of their fight—the surgery. "I'm not sure who I'm mad at."

Shea stood up slowly. Taking the few steps necessary to cross the room, he stopped just behind Lance. He gripped his brother's shoulder. "Don't you think it's time you found out?"

Lance remained silent. How was he supposed to answer? Maybe Eldon had been right. Maybe he was yellow. He didn't think he was scared of El, but in light of all that Shea had posed to him, he was not so sure.

He had blamed his father for everything that had happened ten years ago. Eldon acted like their father—hating Indians on sight. The only positive thing about the man was his love for the Triple-T. Hell, he didn't even show any interest in his own son—just like their father. Had Lance simply shifted that blame to Eldon? Who was really at fault?

"Lance?"

Shea's concerned tone drew Lance from his thoughts.

"You all right?"

Lance managed a forced smile. "Yeah."

"You goin' out after El?"

Lance considered the question. What good would it do? Eldon was as angry as he was himself. And he probably had less understanding of why than Lance did. Best they stay as far away from each other as possible. At least until Lance could get a better grip on things.

A jumble of faces—his father's, Eldon's, Neme's, Tunupiuts's, and even Winter Magic's crowded in on him. Maybe it was time to face his fears . . . and more than one ghost from his past. Maybe then he could straighten things out between him and El.

"You sure you're okay?" Shea asked again.

Lance pursed his lips and nodded. Turning around, he sidestepped the younger man and crossed to the bed. He closed his bag. "Will you see this gets to the ranch for me?"

Shea glanced down at the satchel before flashing Lance a curious stare. "Aren't you comin' back with me?" His gaze followed Lance to the wall peg.

After strapping his gun to his hip, Lance pulled on his coat and grabbed his hat.

"Where you goin'?"

"Down to the livery to rent another horse." Shea opened his mouth in obvious protest, but Lance shot him a reassuring smile. "I need some time to sort things out."

"You goin' to see Tunupiuts?"

"I might end up out there."

"You really think that's a good idea?"

Reaching in his coat pocket, Lance pulled out a pair of leather gloves, then tugged them on. "I don't

know, Shea. I don't know about anything anymore."

Lance looked up through the flutter of snow-
flakes at the dark sky. Morning had brought little
light to the day. Packed like a stuffed bag of gray
cotton balls, the clouds overhead bumped noise-
lessly together.

He scanned the frosted sagebrush, eerie in its
stillness. Not even a jackrabbit skittered about.
Quiet punctuated the uneasy feeling of a pending
storm. Those clouds meant trouble.

He would never make it to the Run of the Red
Deer Ranch before the heavy snowfall set in. He
was still half a day's ride away.

He peered up at Wind Hole. The mountain the
Indians called *Kukwaqta*. He could almost hear the
wind racing over its peak. It always seemed to come
from up there—and it was coming. Of that Lance
was positive. These clouds were bringing at least
another foot of snow—maybe more. And ol' Wind
Hole was sure to send down a rip-snorting gust to
incite the flurries.

No doubt about it. If Lance did not find shelter
and quick, he would find himself caught in the
middle of one hell of a blizzard by midafternoon.
But where to go? Even if he veered off, the Triple-T
was still another three hours' ride. Again, he
checked the low ceiling of white. He would never
make it.

At that moment a mournful moan echoed down
through the pines covering the hillsides. Pulling up
his sheepskin collar closer to his neck, Lance shiv-

ered. He knew what could happen if he was to get caught out in the open.

The cabin. He remembered the little house he had built for him and Neme behind Turtle Mountain. It was only another mile at best. Was it still standing? He would have to chance it. If he hurried, he could make it before the worst of the storm hit. He heeled his horse, urging him north.

By the time Lance had traveled around the base of the small mountain, a full gale had picked up and snow whipped at his face. He squinted through the blinding gusts of white. He could barely make out the building, dark against shifting sheets of ice. Good. It was still there.

Even though it only took him another few moments, the snow was so heavy he lost sight of the house twice.

Legs heavily laden with snow, his horse continued to plod through the deep blanket covering the ground.

"Whoa!" Lance shouted when they stood in front of the house, but his voice was lost to the screaming wind. He tied the horse beneath a partial lean-to he had built years ago to cover firewood. "Sorry, boy!" He slapped the gelding's rump. "It's the best I can do!" He thought he heard the nicker of another horse. He listened to the wind. Nothing.

He trudged toward the cabin, but another gust pushed him back. At last reaching for the door, he thrust it open. The wind's velocity forced him inside in a sudden rush. With a groan of exertion, he slammed the door behind him.

Without warning his feet flew out from under him. His head struck the door. His body hit the floor. Icy steel pressed against his throat. Warm breath fanned his face. Another movement brought the assailant closer still. He could not make out the features in the dark, but he knew there were a pair of desperate eyes boring straight into his.

⚞ 11 ⚟

Winter Magic swallowed the lump in her throat. Knife grasped tightly in her hand, she tried to control her breathing, but her fear held her in its grasp. She peered at the man's form but could see nothing in the darkness. Who was the intruder? No one ever used this place. It had been abandoned long ago.

"Hold on there, friend," the voice behind her blade whispered. "I'm just looking for a warm place to wait out this storm."

She pressed the knife harder and felt it move ever so slightly with the bob of the man's Adam's apple. Good. He was afraid. But then so was she. And now that she had this man, what was she going to do with him? How was she going to get out of this? She could run, but then she would be the one caught freezing in the storm.

Trying to take advantage of what little light there

was filtering in through the weather-beaten shutters, she squinted against the blackness. She could
barely make out the man's outline against the door.

"Could you let up a little on that blade?"

Winter Magic frowned. By his dialect she knew
he must be white. The deep voice of the white man
sounded familiar. She leaned back but kept the
knife threatening any movement.

He slumped down.

"Do not move," she grated.

"Winter Magic?"

She scowled. How did he know her name? "Who
are you, white man?" A throaty chuckle pricked her
hearing.

"It *is* you." He laughed again.

She pushed the knife harder against his neck.
Curled tightly around the bone handle, her fingers
grazed his bristled jaw.

"Hey. It's me, Lance Taggert."

Winter Magic's eyes rounded. How could this be
so? She felt him stir again. "Do not!"

"Wait a minute. I just want to get a match." He
paused. "Okay?"

She tilted her head for a clearer view but could
see him no better. Did he speak the truth? Was this
the Ganoida bui? If not, another man might reach
for a weapon. Still, she had to know. They could not
remain like this for long. The house was not much
warmer than outside. "Move slow."

He did as she instructed.

Something scratched the floor. A spark. A flame.
A small glow lit the man's face yellow-gold.

True to his word, Lance Taggert sat facing her, a
mocking grin spreading his lips thin. He gloved her

hand with his and eased the weapon a space away from him. "Okay now?"

His touch set a new fluttering within her breast. She could not let him see how nervous he made her. Offering him only the slightest look of remorse, she lowered the blade. She sat back on her knees. Her heart was still pounding so hard in her ears that for a moment she thought the raging blizzard might have died. "I could have killed you."

The dark brow over his patched eye peaked slightly higher than the other. "*I* could've killed *you*." He looked down.

Following his gaze, she discovered a gun pointing at her, inches from her middle.

Their stares locked.

The wind whistled through the cracks in the house. The flame wavered.

The Ganoida bui flinched—cursed. He flicked his wrist and the room went dark again.

"There any wood in here?" His voice echoed deep in the empty house.

"Some."

"Where?"

"There." She pointed toward the fireplace as if she thought he could follow her direction in the dark. "The embers still glow."

Rising, he brushed past her. "Damn."

He must have stumbled over something.

"What the hell was that?"

Knowing it must have been her pack, she hid a titter behind a cough.

In a matter of minutes he had a small blaze dancing in the hearth. "There now. That didn't take too long." He grinned at his accomplishment as if it were a great deed.

"*Kai*. It should not have taken long. The embers were still hot. I had it started before you broke in here." She shrugged. "When you rode up, I put it out."

His smile disappeared. His voice flattened. "Oh."

Replacing her knife in its sheath, she stood up and gravitated toward the warmth of the growing fire. She knelt and rubbed her hands together. She barely had time to shirk off her jacket and warm herself from her ride before Lance burst inside. In just the few minutes that she had been without her coat and the fire, her hands had chilled and her teeth had started to chatter.

Lance reached over and picked up her coat. "Here." Moving beside her, he draped her shoulders with it. "You're liable to catch pneumonia."

"Pneumonia?"

"It's like the Pogonip. You know. When your lungs get chilled."

"Ah." She gestured her thanks with a dip of her head.

"What're you doing out here in all of this?" He motioned toward the sound of the wind wailing just beyond the walls.

"Tunupiuts sent me to find you."

He pulled a frown, suspicion marking his features. "Why?"

"He said I should speak to you of an important matter." She avoided eye contact with him. Even in this dim light she could see a strange flicker in his gaze. Could it be the desire he had shown her the day before? She did not look at him, but she could feel his attention, heavy on her body, and it excited her.

"Winter Magic? About yesterday?"

The rich texture of his voice vibrated through the core of her being. She lifted a cautious stare. *"Pisha'?"*

"I'm sorry I—uh—" He seemed to have trouble finding the right way to say whatever it was he was trying to tell her. "Dammit! I shouldn't have let things get out of control like that. It won't happen again."

"But you said—" She bit back the words. She remembered the day before when he had rolled her below him.

"It'll be better next time," he had said.

She gave herself a mental shake. But he had been lost in the heat of passion then. He was clear-headed now. She found herself wondering if he still desired her—if there would be a *next time*.

"Winter Magic?"

She blinked.

"Did you hear me?"

"Pisha'." Pushing the wanton thoughts aside, she stiffened her spine. "Let us not speak of such things. They are forgotten." She watched his posture appear to shrink. It gave her a small measure of triumph.

Seeking another less nerve-wracking path, she unrolled the bearskin robe containing her provisions. "I have food. Are you hungry?"

"Yeah. I rode out from Reno kinda early this morning."

She unwrapped the bundle of deer jerky and a

small bowl of *poyom*. She held out the dried meat and sweet potatoes to him.

"Thanks." He took a wide strip of the meat. He glanced around the interior. "The old place sure has gone to ruin."

Winter Magic quirked a brow. "How is it you know of this house? No one has lived here for a very long time."

"I built it."

Shaking her head, she frowned. "You have been away. Shea and I found this when we were children."

"I lived here—with my wife."

"Neme?" she asked timidly but already knew the answer.

"Yeah." His stare lit with happiness, then dulled just as quickly. "We only had one year together before she was killed."

Winter Magic did not press him further. She knew what had happened to Neme. The woman had broken the law. Winter Magic had been only a child then, but she knew. The people did not speak of the shaman's daughter who had taken a white man for a husband. It would anger the dead to speak of them. Just by saying her name, Winter Magic had tempted his wife's soul up from the spirit world.

She looked back at him. She could see the mark of pain in his gaze and feel his torment, yet she could not help but know a twinge of jealousy over the woman who even from the spirit world still held this man's love. The fact that she now knew that this had been Neme's house with Lance only made it worse.

She selected another small piece of venison for herself. Not wanting him to dwell on the past, she sought to change the subject. She offered him the remainder. "There is more."

He did not even turn his gaze her way, just shook his head.

She did not like this. Inside it was too quiet. Outside the storm raged. After rewrapping the meat, she took both bowl and package and set them on the floor beside her.

The wind wailed mournfully, and she shuddered. It frightened her. She had been told how a person might be taken over by a spirit. Her mind tortured her with these thoughts. Was that Neme's spirit out there? A nervous quiver quaked through her body. She would go crazy if she dwelled on it more. "You were in Reno today?" She spoke more from anxiety than curiosity. She had to get her mind on something else.

"Yeah." He took a bite of the dried meat he still held in his hand, chewed a couple of times, then swallowed.

Watching the simple action of his eating gave her a tiny shiver. What was wrong with her? Did she want to anger Neme? She had to keep herself in check. "Was there more trouble?"

"No." He shook his head and looked at the fire. His gaze filled with pain. "I wanted to talk to Eldon about yesterday. But when I got back home, he had left for Reno. Shea and I went in to find him."

"And did you?"

He rubbed the back of his head and grimaced. "Yeah. I found him all right."

By his expression Winter Magic had a feeling the

brothers' meeting had gone badly. "It did not go well . . . this talk with Eldon?"

He chuckled without mirth. "Not well at all."

"He is still very angry. He hates me, you know. Your brother hates all Indians."

Bringing a knee up to his chest, he took the last bite of his food. He reached down and picked up a chip of wood, then tossed it into the flames. "Eldon hates himself."

Lowering her gaze, Winter Magic shuddered. She did not like to see the Ganoida bui look so unhappy. She felt sorry for him. Maybe even a little sorry for Eldon Taggert. How awful to hate oneself.

"Did you ever know our pa?" Lance asked.

"*Kai.*" She tried to think of something pleasant to say about the man, but none of her people had ever referred to him as anything other than a hard, unfeeling person. "I have only heard one thing about him. He was very strong." It was not a lie. Tunupiuts had told Yitakam of a fight that he had had with the man many years ago. Neither had been the victor.

Lance snorted. "I'll bet you've heard a lot more than that." His brow wrinkled and his expression looked pained. "I never could understand his hatred of the Indians. I guess he didn't like them being here first."

"Indians have always lived here. Maidu, Washo, Bannock, Paiutes—all have always hunted and lived in this valley. It has always been our *Tasup,* our wild game place."

He held up a hand. "I know what you're saying. It's just that Pa never understood that. He never tried. And he sure as hell didn't like sharing any part of this valley with anybody but white folks. And most of them he barely tolerated."

"It is a very sad thing not to share."

"I asked him once why he hated Indians."

Winter Magic's curiosity was piqued. She had always heard that Lance's father was a mean man. "What was his answer?"

"He didn't say. He just cuffed me and told me it wasn't any of my business. I guess we'll never know."

Retrieving a small pouch of tea from within the folds of her bearskin, she frowned. She had neglected to bring a pot to brew it in. She set it aside and stood. Moving into the shadows, she began to plunder the corners of the barren room, searching, hoping to find something she could use.

"What're you doing?"

"I have some *wukuikum*, but I forgot to bring my cooking pot for water. Maybe there's something here. There was another white eye that lived—" Her gaze darted to his. The slur on his heritage caught in her throat.

His body tensed and he shot her a glare.

"I did not mean to insult you."

He smiled slowly. "It's okay. I've been called worse."

She pulled her upper lip between her teeth. She had no wish to offend him—even if her people did not need him.

"Here. I'll help." He rooted around the opposite side of the room, digging through the decaying scraps of wood. "I found something." Metal clinked. He held up a battered kettle. "It's got a rusted-out hole near the top, but I think we can make it work—"

A sudden gust of wind clawed through the shutters. It knocked the boards loose over the window, and the bar holding the shutters together fell to the floor.

Winter Magic yelped. The corner of one board struck her forehead. Heart lodging in her throat, she threw her hands up to shield her face.

Snow burst into the house.

She fought to grab the wooden brace, but the gale was too strong for her. Her hair whipped across her eyes.

Appearing from across the room, Lance grabbed her arms and pushed her back.

Through a sheet of icy wind she watched him slam the shutters closed and set the remains of the broken latch in place.

"You all right?"

She nodded even though she could feel the wood's bite above her brow.

"You're hurt." Lance rushed to her side.

"*Kai*. It causes no pain." It was only a small lie. She touched the wound, but more than a trickle of blood smeared her fingers. "It is not bad."

"Bad enough." Lance pulled her toward the fire. He pushed her down to sit. "Let me see."

"It is only a scratch." It did hurt a little but not enough for this much fuss. "All wounds to the face bleed a lot."

He took off his coat, then pulled out his shirttail. "Let me see your knife."

"It is no more than a scratch," she protested

again, yet she handed him the blade. It felt good to have him worry over her. Maybe he did like her.

He cut a nick into the heavy cloth, then ripped a strip from the bottom of his shirt. "Hold this to your head." Jumping up, he retrieved the kettle from the floor where he had dropped it.

"Where are you going?"

"To get some snow. I want to clean that up."

Returning, he set the kettle next to the flames. When the water had boiled, he dumped out the *poyom* and poured some water into the clay bowl. He took the rag away from her and washed it out. Then, cradling the back of her head with one hand, he rinsed out the cloth. "Now. Let's see to that cut."

Winter Magic flinched at the heat of the coarse material on her tender skin.

"See, it does hurt."

"Only a little." She watched the taut play of his muscles beneath his shirt as he tended her forehead. She remembered the strength of their embrace. Her heart lurched with the nearness of him.

"Lean forward." His command was brusque, but his tone was husky.

Without protest she did as he instructed. She closed her eyes and inhaled.

He smelled clean, yet earthy, a hint of sagebrush clinging to his skin. He shifted beside her, and his knees brushed her leg.

The simple action sent a shiver of excitement through her. Had Owl Eyes made her feel this way? She did not think so. Why did Lance Taggert?

"You're right. It's not bad at all." His voice soothed her as much as the gentle strokes he applied to her wound.

The contrast between his callused palm and comforting hold felt good against her neck. Relaxing under his ministration, she moaned.

His hands stilled.

Why had he stopped? Languidly she opened her eyes. Her heart lodged in her throat. Without realizing it she had moved closer, to within inches of his face, her mouth dangerously close to his.

Like a pale crystal, his one eye glimmered in the firelight, then darkened. He eased nearer.

She pulled back.

His fingers pressed into her flesh, holding her still.

She flinched. Instinctively she grabbed his shoulders, bracing herself apart from him.

He slid his hands lightly down her arms. He drew her closer.

Their eyes met.

A rush of heat flooded her body. Her hands felt hot where they gripped him. She became aware of his breathing, heavy, rapid, like an animal stalking another. Her pulse quickened. She was frightened, but not of him—of herself. She wanted him— needed his touch. But this was wrong.

"I know I said it wouldn't happen again, but I can't let go of you." There was a roughness in his voice, a possessiveness she had never imagined before.

She held her breath. She should stop him. "Lance, this is"—she swallowed—"not right."

"Why? Because my skin's white and yours is red? I'm not my father."

She pulled back a little. "I know who *you* are." She thought of the house they were in and the day before when he had called her Neme. "But . . . who am *I*?"

He stared at her long and hard, his expression awash with warmth and understanding, a tiny flicker of desire dancing just beneath his steady gaze. He reached up and stroked her cheekbone. "*You* are Komeni Tu'madai." Feather-light, he brushed her lips with his. "And this . . . is *not* wrong." He pulled her tighter, crushing her to him.

She moaned against his mouth. Her lips parted. Her tongue met his, probing, tasting. Her hands strayed to his chest. Her head whirled like the screaming storm outside. What was she doing? No. She could not let this happen. What about the promise she had made to herself? She could not allow anything to happen to him like it did to Owl Eyes.

His fingers twined in her hair at the back of her head. He groaned, a husky sound that vibrated from deep in his throat.

It caught her off guard, reeling her senses, stirring her with alarm. "*Kai*, Lance." She pushed away from him, yet remained in his embrace. "We cannot do this."

"Why?" His voice was strained.

Beneath her palms, his heartbeat thrummed. Still shaking with desire, she took a breath. "There was another man long ago—"

"So what? I don't care about him."

"I must tell you—"

"Then tell me, damn it!"

She swallowed. "I am not a maiden." Her cheeks flamed. Embarrassment overcame her composure, and she hesitated. She had to make him understand. She had to word it just right. But instead of gaining her strength, that single suspended moment caused her defeat.

With a surge of male energy he gripped her hair and tugged her head, tilting it backward. "I want you and I think you want me, too—that's all that matters." He kissed her again, his mouth crushing hers, his hunger devouring her, his need stealing her breath.

Liquid heat coursed through her being. Her mind fought for control, but the pleasuring of her body won. She lost herself in the pure want of him. Her hands slid around his waist and up his back. He felt hard and lean and powerful.

She met his tongue with hers, touched it, teased it, then pushed hers deeper into his mouth. She clutched his back, digging her nails into his flesh. She could not stop herself. She was like a woman possessed. Had Neme taken her body? The thought frightened her, yet excited her more. No. It was Winter Magic in this man's arms. She knew that, and so did he.

A ragged moan rumbled in her throat when he broke the kiss. His mouth burned a path down her neck. Beneath his knowing fingers, the buttons on her shirt fell open. Her breath caught as the sudden chill of one hand cupped a breast. His thumb rubbed her nipple, already taut from the infusion of cold and the heat of his touch. She arched against him. Never had she felt like this. With Owl Eyes it had been hurried and clumsy. With Owl Eyes . . . The name faded in her mind.

Lance's head slipped lower, nibbling her skin as he inched his way downward. He took her breast into his mouth; his other hand moved to her back.

She gasped and drew him closer still. Shock-waves of pleasure rocked her core. She needed to feel him, his hands, his mouth all at once.

His tongue was like liquid flame lapping her nipple. He sucked her fully into his mouth. He moved his support from her back. The dishes clattered behind her, and he pushed her down to the bearskin robe. His free hand returned to her body just beneath one shoulder. He spread her shirt apart, then slipped his palm lightly over her belly, around her navel, and down, to the first rivet on her pants.

Anticipation shivered through her. The naked thought of him being inside her became unbearable. Her mind screamed his name. Her mouth went dry. Her breathing grew shallow. She had never known such hunger.

His fingers pressed her abdomen, stroking her with sweet, painful circles. Atop the denim he slid his hand lower, gliding across the coarse fabric to her thighs.

With shameless abandon, she parted her legs for him. She seemed to have no will of her own, no strength, nor desire to stop him. Her fingers raked through his hair, pressing his mouth harder against her breast. The light stubble of his beard teased her skin, driving her mad with need.

He pulled away from her.

The sudden break in contact jolted her senses. Beneath heavy lids she watched him move in silent fascination.

Raising up on one arm, he reached down and slowly unbuttoned her pants. He bent his head and kissed her stomach where each rivet parted the fabric baring her skin. He looked back at her, his gaze beckoning her consent.

She smiled. She was his to do with as he pleased.

Gripping the edge of her pants, he pushed them down. He coaxed her buttocks up with a light nudge of his hand at her side.

Planting her feet against the floor, she lifted her hips.

He shoved the weighty garment down until she lay naked to his impassioned gaze.

Her stomach quivered. No man had ever looked at her like this before.

He leaned over and touched the curls at the juncture of her legs with his lips.

Sucking in a breath, she shuddered. She tipped her head back and squeezed her eyes closed. Her body felt fluid, her blood molten, her skin burned.

He positioned himself fully between her legs.

Instinctively she scooted higher on the robe, making room for him to stretch out below her.

His hands slipped beneath the back of her thighs, lifting them until her knees were bent on either side of his head.

With the first touch of his tongue to her womanly flesh, she nearly screamed out with the thrill. The second—she did. Her body exploded with excitement. She could not control her need. Something akin to thunderbolts electrified her senses. Tiny charges of sweet pain collided in her veins, bursting in a frenzy of fluid heat.

He probed deeper, kissing her opening. She had never known such torture. But the blessed strokes of his tongue brought only the sweetest of torment.

Lost in a glorious merging of heaven and hell, she writhed uncontrollably.

His hands trailed up her body, skittering across her skin to her breasts. With gentle fingers he squeezed her nipples, twisting them lightly back and forth.

Her nerves became a jitter of movement, building steadily, mounting one on top of the other until— A shockwave of pleasure racked her soul, jolting her senses, exploding in a million shards of light. She screamed out his name in the purest rapture she had ever known.

Clutching the fur beneath her, she rocked her head from side to side. She bit her bottom lip, the salty taste of blood mingling with her mouth's musky flavor. Basking in the receding passion, she did not notice that Lance had moved until she heard the light tinkle of his belt buckle.

She opened her eyes.

A sheen of moisture covered his face. His one visible eye darkened as his gaze devoured every inch of her. He ripped his shirt from his shoulders, his muscles flexing with his quick movements. He tossed it to the floor, then pulled off his boots and pants.

Towering above her in the firelight, his lean body glistened gold. Corded muscles across broad shoulders boasted of a man unafraid of hard labor. Large hands, larger than she had noticed before, dwarfed her own. But it was the sight of his maleness that caused a tiny gasp to escape her throat. Never had she seen the full arousal of a man.

He knelt between her thighs. He cupped her

bottom, lifting her hips to meet his penetration. Probing, pushing a little at a time, he entered her.

She threw her arms around his neck and pulled him to her.

He rocked slowly at first, then pumped a little faster until the force of his movements pounded into her with furious thrusts.

She tightened around him, basking in the raw maleness of him, meeting his every plunge with a lunge of her own. Her face burned against the friction of his unshaven jaw. It hurt, but she did not care—it was her only pain.

All at once his expression grew strained, his muscles taut. Then a pure sweet fury unlike anything she had ever known burst inside her. Clutching his hair, she met his climax with the full savagery of her own.

They held each other until the spasms of their passion ebbed and a gentle fluxing of sated desire embraced their souls.

After a few minutes Winter Magic's breathing became labored beneath his weight.

"God, I'm sorry. I must be crushing you." Lance rolled off of her. And with their bodies' parting, he groaned. Turning on his side, he pulled her close, then rested a hand atop one breast. He kissed the corner of her eye. "That was wonderful."

Lids closed, she moaned in agreement, then smiled. She reached up to grasp his arm but stopped mid-action. She had something in her hand. She raised it to the glow of the fire and squinted. Her eyes rounded. Clutched in her palm was Lance's eye patch. She shot a nervous glance his way. She could not see his face clearly. Her body shadowed his features. Was he looking at her?

Feather-soft against her ear, his slow rhythmic breathing answered her question. He had fallen asleep.

Closing her hand around the swatch of black, she turned, facing him, and sighed. *She* was not about to go to sleep. She would lie here and watch him—all night if she had to. His gaze was so startlingly beautiful, she had to see both of his eyes again.

She pulled the sides of the bearskin over their nakedness, then lay there patiently beside him, contentment lulling her body.

The firelight dimmed. The storm had died. Her lids grew heavy. She felt his arms tighten around her, and she snuggled closer to his warmth.

She jerked herself to wakefulness. Even though she was tired, she could not allow herself to relax too much. Her eyes snapped open, then slowly they fluttered downward again.

He might be determined to keep that one eye concealed from view, but she was just as determined to see it again. And even as she drifted over the edge of slumber, her mind held on to her purpose. *She* would not fall asleep before seeing his eyes. . . .

⮺ 12 ⮺

Winter Magic awoke with a start. The bearskin was tucked gently around her, but she was alone in its warmth. Lance. Where was he? Had he left? Panic lodged in her throat. She had not yet told him of the Great Spirit's message. And Nighthawk would be angry with her if she did not bring him back for the celebration of the child.

The fire crackled behind her. Was it still burning from the night before? She turned over. Light spilling through a half-open shutter stabbed her eyes. She groaned, blinked, then shaded them with her hand.

"Well. Good morning, Tu'madai." Silhouetted against the white glare, Lance stood naked at the window. He looked down at her.

Relieved to see him, she smiled. For a minute she had thought he was gone—worse yet, that last night had only been a dream. Looking past him out the window, she saw that only a light fluttering of snow remained of the blizzard. "The storm has passed?"

He nodded. "Did you sleep well?" A hint of morning huskiness laced his voice.

She sighed. She did not think she had ever woken up to a more beautiful sound. Winter Magic fell back on the pallet and stretched catlike. "*Pisha'.* Very well."

Arms raised, fingers extended, she remembered the eye patch and froze. She bolted upright, threw the fur aside, and began to root around for the small covering. She must have lost it in the folds during her sleep. Sleep! She had not meant to do that.

"What're you looking for?" He came to stand beside her, then squatted.

When she looked at him, her shoulders slumped in exasperation. He was wearing the black patch. She released a heavy groan. "Nothing."

A slow smile tugged at the corners of his mouth, and he chuckled.

"What is it?" Instinctively she reached up and smoothed her hair.

He shook his head. "It's nothing."

"It is something, or you would not laugh at me."

"I'm not laughing at you." His expression sobered, yet not quite.

With an indignant tilt of her chin Winter Magic glanced around the cabin. "I do not see anyone else."

Lance chuckled again.

"See." She stiffened her spine. Then, thrusting out her lower lip, she folded her arms across her stomach. "You laugh at me."

Still chuckling, he reached for her face, but she turned it away from him.

She flinched.

"Hey." Touching her cheek, he coaxed her around to look at him. He brushed the tender spot on her chin. "How did this happen?"

"You did it."

He raised his brows, amusement crinkling the corners of his eyes. "How did I do that?"

"With your—" Still angry, she gestured to his beard.

"Oh, I—uh—see." His expression sobered, and he rubbed his face. "Guess I need a shave, huh."

She did not answer. She could not look at him. It hurt to think he would make fun of her.

"Tu'madai." His voice softened. "I really wasn't laughing at you. It's just that—well—"

"What?" This was not funny.

He cleared his throat, and his expression grew serious. "I didn't mean to hurt your feelings. It's just that . . ."

"You have said that!" She was really beginning to get angry.

"I've never met anyone like you."

"I do not understand. I am no different from any other woman." She began to get angry. She squared her shoulders.

"Oh, yes you are."

"How?"

"Well . . ." He gestured toward her posture. "Just look at you."

Frowning, her gaze flitted downward. She could see nothing that made her unique—nothing that would set her apart from any other woman she knew.

"I've known proud women before, but—" His gaze strayed to her breasts, and the beginnings of another grin pulled at his mouth.

Her cheeks flamed, and she suddenly understood his meaning. After last night she had not realized he would be disturbed by her nudity. Reaching down, she gripped the fur and clutched it over herself. She cut her gaze away. "Forgive me. I have offended you once again. I am a woman without shame." She bowed her head.

"No, you're not." He paused. "Look at me."

She could not. Her uncle had been right about her, and now she would have to go and pray again.

"Winter Magic." A note of irritation marked his tone.

She lifted a timid gaze.

Gathering her hands in his, he leaned closer. "You haven't offended me. It's me that's offended you."

"*Kai*, Lance. I should not have—"

"Just listen to me for a minute. It's been a long time since I've been with a woman. Especially one as beautiful as you."

Her heart soared. He thought she was beautiful. No one but her aunt and Moon Dove had ever said this to her. She had not truly believed them, but now— Maybe it was the gentle quality of his voice. Maybe it was the caring look in his eye, but somehow she knew he had spoken from his heart. It did not matter if it was true; it only mattered that *he* believed it.

"If anyone needs to apologize, it's me."

"You?"

"For years, whenever I've slept with a woman, it was because I needed her." He quirked a brow. "Do you understand?"

"*Pisha'*. It is the same for all men, is it not?"

He shook his head. "I mean, I *needed* the release of a woman's body. But last night . . . I *wanted* you." He peered deeper. "Do you see the difference? A need is like—like . . . food. You have to have it. But wanting something is like . . ." He hesitated, his expression puzzled. "Have you ever had a piece of sugar candy?"

"*Pisha'*. Sometimes my friend Moon Dove brings some to the children at our ranch."

"Did you like it?"

She nodded. She began to realize the comparison he was trying to make. "Wanting is like the candy."

"Exactly." He lifted one of her hands and kissed its back.

The bearskin slipped from her grasp. She started to catch it, but he stilled her movement. "That's how it was for me with you last night."

She blushed. A warm glow filled her heart, spreading throughout her body with the growing intensity of his stare. No one had ever said anything so nice to her. "I, too, knew great pleasure from your touch, Lance."

"I'm sorry I laughed at you. I didn't mean to hurt your feelings. It's just that every time I've seen you, somehow or another your—uh—" He gestured towards her breasts. "You've been uncovered."

More than a little self-conscious, she lifted the robe higher. Her gaze fell to a button on the bottom of his open shirt. Uncomfortable beneath his stare, she shifted her weight. "It is something that I, too, have noticed. The first time I was angry. I wanted to show you that you could not disgrace me." Her head sank a little lower. "But I shamed myself."

He stroked the back of her hand with his thumb.

It sent a shiver rippling up her arm. She took a breath. "The other times I did not know until . . . it was too late. I am sorry it disturbed you."

He lifted her chin with his free hand. "Don't be. You're the best disturbance I've had in a long—long time." His hand slipped down to the fur. He traced the edge with a finger, then tugged it loose until it fell to her waist. His eyes darkened.

The sudden cold caused her to shudder.

He cupped the underswell of one breast and brushed her nipple with his thumb. He leaned forward, his lips a breath from hers. "Like you, they're beautiful."

Even before she felt his mouth on hers, she closed her eyes and surrendered to him. Again, she forgot the purpose for which she had been sent to find him. She forgot that she had not yet seen the eye behind his black patch again. She forgot everything except the man, his touch, and the magical way he made her feel.

In the afterglow of their lovemaking Winter Magic lay in Lance's tender embrace. So much had happened in so short a time. A week ago she had not known this man even existed; now she lay contented in his arms. How bewildering were the ways of the Great Spirit.

The first moment she had set eyes on Lance

Taggert, the Great Spirit had thrust the white man into her life. They had collided headlong. She did not yet fully understand the purpose in this. Nor why the bond between her and the Ganoida bui had come together so quickly. She was content that the Great Spirit would reveal his purpose when it served his need. For now it did not matter. She only knew what *she* had to do. She must tell Lance of his destiny and, if need be, guide him down the path the Great Spirit had set him upon.

Cuddled against his chest, she delighted in the way his steady breathing whispered warm across her neck. After so long believing there would never be a man for her, it felt good to finally have someone with whom she could share her life.

The thought triggered a less pleasant one. Could she only be a lure sent by the Great Spirit to catch the Ganoida bui?

Why had *she* been chosen? Another woman would have been better. She had promised herself she would never allow her heart the bond of a man's love. And now she had broken that promise in a moment of weakness. What good would come of this?

The Ganoida bui would not take her to his heart. His bed was something different. A man needed a woman. Yet he had said it was not need but want, had he not?

No. She gave herself a mental shake. This was only the foolish hope of a lonely woman. Even if he had not said as much, she knew that only Neme would ever hold his heart. What had she been thinking? Neme was a spirit. How could Winter

Magic hope to win Lance from a shadow of his past? He had lived with it too long.

The Great Spirit had given her a task. Her purpose was clear and much more important than her own selfish desire. Lance Taggert had been brought full circle. The Great Spirit had delivered him back to this valley for a single design. The valley must not be tainted with blood. Her people and his must walk together. She would not allow herself to forget again. "Lance?"

"Hmm?"

She turned onto her back and stared up at the decaying roof. "I told you that my uncle sent me to find you, do you remember?"

"Mmm-hmm." Raising on one elbow, he rested his head in his hand. He drew tiny circles across her stomach with his fingertips. "You never did say why, though."

Now was her chance. "It is because of a message given to me by the Great Spirit."

"Really?" He sounded amused. "And what message was that?"

Ignoring his tone, she continued. "You remember yesterday when you came to the hot springs and I was praying?"

He nodded.

"Just before you rode into my camp, I had asked the Great Spirit for a sign." She cut her gaze to him, then lowered her voice. "*You* were that sign."

He chuckled. "Me?" He shook his head. "*I* was cold."

"Do not laugh, Lance." Pushing him down atop the bearskin, she rolled over to face him. "You will anger the Great Spirit. It is an honor to be chosen by him."

Smiling playfully, he took her hand and held it. "I'm sure it is, but I'm not an Indian. What would your Great Spirit want with me?"

"He is not mine. We are his—all people are his—both Indian and white."

"Look, Winter Magic." He tapped the end of her nose. "I'm sure you believe this, but—"

She slapped at his hand. She was starting to get angry. Why did he not listen? Frustrated, she threw herself back to the floor with a huff. She grabbed one side of the fur and yanked it over herself, then folded her arms over her chest. "This is important, Lance. You do not even know of the message yet, and you already make jokes. This is not good."

He regained his earlier position. "Okay, so what's this message?" He still smiled.

"Stop!" She tried to sound firm. She had to make him understand.

His expression sobering, he stared at her for a long moment. "You're serious about this, aren't you?"

"It is a thing to be most serious about. The Great Spirit does not choose a warrior to defend his wishes carelessly."

"Warrior? Defend?" He chuckled again.

It brought her pain to see him laugh this time.

He must have noticed, because he stopped short. He laid his hand atop hers and coaxed them apart. Then, flexing his fingers in between hers, he grasped her hand. "I'm very flattered that you think he has chosen me. I'm just not sure I believe it's possible."

Winter Magic's eyes flew wide. "You do not believe the Great Spirit can do this?"

He shrugged. "I don't know what I believe. Look, Tu'madai." He exhaled a breath. "I'm nobody special—"

"How do you know?" She *was* angry now. Heedless of her nakedness, she bolted upright. She shifted around so that she faced him fully. "White eyes think they have all the answers. They think they can control everything that happens to them. But they cannot." She took a firm hold on her thoughts. "Only the Great Spirit can know what is to be, and what is not. It is He who decides all things."

"And you don't think we have any say-so in what we do?"

"*Pisha'*. We can follow His path, or we can run away from it." She paused, allowing her words to hit their mark. "Always, in the end, we do as our destiny bids us do."

Rising, Lance faced off in front of her. "So you're telling me that I've come home because of some preordained bullshit."

Winter Magic gasped. Anger seething inside her, she narrowed her eyes. "You are not here because it is what *you* want. You are here because of the Great Spirit."

Lance snorted. "Hell, woman! I don't *want* to be here. I'm here because I'm not good enough to do the job I was trained to do anymore."

Winter Magic winced. Did he mean here in the valley or here with her? The latter caused her the greatest torment. Struggling up to her feet, she kicked the bearskin aside. She could not think. She found her pants.

"Where're you going?"

After stepping into them and pulling them up, she grabbed her moccasins. Once she had them on her feet, she was like a mad animal, plundering the room in a blind rage, searching for her shirt. She could not see it. Spying the bright colors of her coat, she raced to it and snatched it up.

"I asked where you're going." Lance jumped up and grabbed her by the shoulders.

She dropped her coat. She shoved him back, not far, but enough so she was able to grab her coat and put it on.

Seizing her again, he snapped her head up to look at him.

"Let me go!" She fought his hold, flailing and squirming with all her strength. But to no advantage. She clawed at his face. "Let go of me, you stupid white eye!"

He veered away, but her nails caught in the cord of his eye patch.

She stopped. Gasped. Blinked.

For a moment the cabin appeared to spin around them. They stood silent, staring at each other.

He arched a brow. "Yeah. I guess I am."

Winter Magic's heart pounded in her ears. The eye she had so badly wanted to see was suddenly revealed to her. Pale as a moonbeam, lighter than his right by a single shade, his left eye bore into hers. She looked at her hand. The patch was in her fist. What had she done?

So sudden was his release of her, she nearly fell backward with its swiftness.

He stalked across the room and retrieved his pants from where he had tossed them the previous night. Keeping his back to her, he pulled them on.

She had been right. His injured eye was as handsome as the other one. She had longed to see it but not like this. She had never meant for this to happen. Now she had humiliated him.

"I am sorry, Ganoida bui." She hoped he would hear the sincerity in her voice. "I did not mean to—"

"Don't call me that!"

"I am sorry, Lance." She held the eye patch out to him, but he did not see her.

His back remained toward her. Head bent, he set his hands on his hips. A throaty sigh escaped his body in a slow exhale.

She had to do something, but what? Tears stung her eyes. "I did not mean to hurt you." Cautiously she made her way across the room, halting an arm's length away. She held the patch out to him. Her body trembled. "Please, Lance. I did not mean it."

He continued to ignore her.

There. It was over. She had ruined everything. Reaching out, she took his hand.

He flinched at her touch, but she held firmly to her intentions. Tears scalding down her cheeks, she carefully pressed the patch into his palm. No words came to her. There was nothing more to say. She felt helpless—as if someone twisted her insides. Why did he not speak? Her gaze traveled the width of his shoulders and up to the fine black hairs below his nape.

Even if he spoke in anger, it would be better than his silence. She waited motionless—hoping. But he did not. A tiny whimper caught in her throat. She had to leave. He no longer wanted her here. She turned away and hurried out the door—and out of Lance Taggert's life.

The sharp glare of sunlight against snow blinded her almost as much as the tears. She trudged as fast as she could through the deep snowdrifts, around the side of the small house to where Kozo stood tethered. Running full-tilt, she slammed against the side of the animal with a heartsick groan. Salty tears fell in earnest now.

What was she going to do? She had failed in her duty to the Great Spirit, failed in her obligation to Nighthawk, and failed to keep her own promise to herself. However would she set things right again? Never had she felt so discouraged and useless. She cried harder.

"Who's running now?" Lance slipped his arms around her waist.

She whirled around. Beneath tear-soaked lashes, she stared up at him.

Beautiful eyes, one gray, one white, smiled down at her.

"Your patch—I gave it back—"

He lifted it up. "What I have to say to you, I want to say without it. I want you to see that it's the truth and that it comes from inside."

"I thought you were mad at me—"

"Shh." He touched a finger to her lips. He slipped his hands down and clasped them behind her. "I believed in the Great Spirit a long time ago. Neme taught me to trust in Him then as you do now. She told me I was special, too. She told me that the Great Spirit had smiled on us—that we were good together." He peered up and squinted at a sky so blue it hurt to look at it. "And I guess we were— while it lasted. But then she died, and my new little girl, too."

Winter Magic found her voice. "Is that why you are angry with the Great Spirit?"

"No. At myself. I should've known better than to stay here with her. Neither her people, nor mine, approved. It was against Indian law for an Indian woman to marry a white man."

Winter Magic bit the inside of her jaw. She was having a hard time concentrating on Neme. The same law still held for Winter Magic herself.

He looked down at her. "Neme was one of your own people. Did you know that?"

Hesitating, Winter Magic swallowed. She could not lie. "Her name is not unknown to me."

"Then you know what happened to her?"

She nodded reluctantly.

His stare probed hers but then relaxed. He loosened his grip on her hand. "I guess I knew that." He did not speak for a moment. His gaze moved to the distance.

Kozo stamped his foot.

"Lance?" Her voice quivered.

He did not speak.

"Do you hate my people for what they did to Neme?"

He said nothing.

Her anxiety mounted.

Slowly his head began to shake back and forth. He looked down at her. "I don't know why. It hadn't even occurred to me that I should until Shea brought it up."

"Shea hates us?"

A tiny smile tugging at his mouth offered her a glimmer of hope.

"No. He just pointed out a few facts I had never considered. He told me how I blamed Pa for all my pain, Neme's death, the baby's, my life, everything."

"Your life has not been good?"

"I never thought about it as being good or bad. It just was."

"Was? I do not understand."

"I haven't had a life for ten years. I had a job—and I was damn good at it. Until this happened." He gestured toward his injured eye.

"What happened?"

"I got careless. A man cut me. I almost died, probably should have, too." He pursed his lips and paused.

Winter Magic could feel the pain and suffering flowing out of him. Her heart constricted.

"It's been so long since I really felt anything besides hate and unhappiness. I thought I was dead inside, to tell you the truth."

Another chance. In her excitement she rushed the moment. "But that is why you have been chosen."

Lance frowned.

"You are to be reborn, Lance Taggert. The Great Spirit has given you a second chance at life."

He tightened his clasp at her back and grinned. "You don't give up, do you?"

She started to protest.

"Listen to me," he commanded. "I need some time to digest everything you've said." He reached up and caressed her cheek, then combed his fingers through her hair to the back of her head. "And even more time to think about what happened last night."

Somewhere overhead a hawk called out.

Both looked up, then slowly met each other's gaze again.

"I left Reno yesterday to be by myself for a while. I need to try and sort some things out." He smiled playfully. "I seem to be doing a lot of that lately. But then, with the storm and you—"

Her heart plummeted. "You were unhappy to find me here."

"No." He leaned into her face. "I was very *happy* to find you here. I just couldn't believe you were, that's all."

"And now?"

"I'm still happy about it . . . just a little confused is all."

"I, too, am confused, Lance. But I believe we can—"

"I know you believe it; I'm just not sure where I stand. I don't want you to be hurt. And I'm not sure if I have anything to give you, or if what I have is enough."

"But you are the sign. The Great Spirit has told me that you have come back to help my people."

"Help you? Woman, don't you hear what I'm saying? I can't even fix my own life."

"That is why *I* am here—to help you fix your life," she said, desperate to make him understand. But suddenly it was *she* that understood. The Great Spirit had brought this man to the valley for more than one purpose. He needed a woman, and she needed a man. Both were lonely. Each would make the other complete. But what about her people's law? How would they deal with that?

"Tu'madai." He brushed her lips with his thumb. "You're still very young. You haven't seen all that I have. You don't understand that things don't always get *fixed* just because we want them to." He leaned back a space and took a deep breath. "I need you to do something for me. Will you do it?"

"*Pisha'*. I will do it." She felt a sudden chill whip up in between the opening of her jacket and Lance. She remembered her shirt, but tried to concentrate on what he was about to ask.

"I need you to go home."

"Without you?"

He nodded.

She stiffened. "But I cannot. Tunupiuts told me to bring you back with me."

"Yeah." Lance cocked his head. "Why is that? You never said."

Remembering the birth, her face warmed. "He wishes you to stand with him when he presents his new son to the tribe."

His expression brightened. "Yitakam had a boy?"

She shrugged. "I do not know. The child had not been born yet when I left. But soon—"

"So he thinks it's going to be another boy, huh?"

"*Pisha'*. That is why he asked that I bring his old friend back to share this with him."

"Hmph. What's he going to do if it's a girl?"

Winter Magic frowned. "Yitakam has always had boy children."

"Yeah, well, it'd serve Tunupiuts right if she had a girl this time. Yeah, I think I'd like to be there for that one." His eyes glimmered with some unknown humor. "Is the whole tribe going to be there?"

She nodded. "He sent a rider to tell them of the birth at the same time I left."

"Okay. I'll come, but later. You go on home."

"But—"

He turned her around and hoisted her up on Kozo. "You tell Tunupiuts I'll be there."

"Why do you not come now?"

"Look. If I remember right, things like this are a cause for a big celebration?"

"*Pisha*."

"Well, like I told you. I still need some time by myself. Besides . . ." He winked. "It's bad luck to come without a present for the parents, isn't it?"

She thought about the new cradle board she had woven to give to her aunt and uncle. "It is so."

He rubbed an intimate hand up her leg. "Trust me, Tu'madai. I will come. Trust me?"

She did not want to leave him, but she dared not push him further on the matter. "I trust you."

"Good." He tugged her arm, pulling her down to him. He kissed her then. A warm, languid kiss that trapped any doubts she had and sent them scurrying.

When he pulled away, he was grinning. "And Tu'madai?"

She secured Kozo's reins in her grasp. "*Pisha*'?"

"You might want to put this on before you go." He tossed a light blue bundle up at her.

Kozo tossed his head.

She blanched but grabbed the garment. It was the shirt she could not find.

He took a step back, then slapped Kozo on the rump.

The animal sidestepped away, but she held him steady. Heat flamed her face. "I could not find it."

Backing away, he turned for the house, then waved. "It was under the bearskin."

She smiled her thanks, then wheeled Kozo around and started for the ranch. She would have to hurry home and make ready for his visit. She would have to unroll her white deerskin dress and rub it soft again. Unroll her dress? Her robe. She had forgotten it as well.

She pulled the bit against the horse's mouth, then turned in her seat. "Wait! Lance. My robe." But it was too late for him to hear. She had ridden off too far, and he had already disappeared around the cabin.

⚞13⚟

On his way back from Reno to the Run of the Red Deer Ranch, Lance stopped at the edge of Long Valley Creek to give his horse a drink. After Winter Magic's departure, he had remained at the cabin for the rest of the day and night. He had only been able to make one decision about himself and the Indian woman. Go slow. Past that he was still as confused as ever.

The things she had told him about his being some chosen warrior sent by the Great Spirit to end the turmoil between the Indians and the whites still had him completely baffled. Why did she believe that of him?

He swung his leg over the animal's head and dismounted, then dropped the reins so that the roan was free to lean down. He checked the heavy twine securing the present he had bought for Yitakam.

The spindle-framed rocker still remained tightly

bound across the horse's rump. He shook his head at the amazing web of string he had had to use to tie it down. If the chair had been any bigger, he would have had to hire a packhorse to bring it along. "Sure hope she likes it."

He moved to the saddlebags and checked their contents. Wrapped with a pink satin bow, the box of H. Upman Lansdale Cigars he had bought for Nighthawk appeared to be unharmed by the ride. He chuckled. Even if Yitakam did have a boy, it would be enough to see Nighthawk's face when Lance told him why he had chosen that color of ribbon. It would be a good joke.

He leaned back and stretched. He had been riding since daybreak, and after only a few hours in the saddle, he was starting to feel the strain of his recuperation. Six months of little to no riding on a horse while he had been laid up with his injury and surgery was starting to show in his muscles. He had assured the doctor in Chicago he would take it easy. Hmph. He had gotten more rest in the hospital with all those nurses running in and out checking his temperature all the time. Nothing had been easy since he had gotten home.

He thought of the paper-wrapped package in the saddlebag on the other side. Would Winter Magic like her gift? He hoped she would not be offended by the undergarment. But if she were truly going to try the life of a white woman, she had best make good use of that frilly little— What had that Madam Rochette called it again? A chemise? Yeah. He had enjoyed listening to the little woman's French accent, but she sure had been hard to understand.

It had taken nearly an hour of pacing in front of

the ladies' store waiting for the different women going in and out to finish making their purchases and leave, but he finally managed to get up the nerve to go inside. And by then Madam Rochette was about to close. Buying that little chemise had been one of the toughest things he had ever done—not to mention embarrassing.

The horse pawed at the ground.

"You had enough, boy?" Lance hooked the stirrup over the horn and tightened the animal's belly strap.

The roan snorted, then pawed at the thin surface of ice blocking him from his drink.

"Here." Lance moved around in front of the animal and stomped the frozen water with his bootheel until it broke free.

The horse suddenly whinnied. His ears pricked up. Lifting his nose into the air, he snorted.

"What is it, boy?" Lance turned and looked all around them. Nothing but frostbitten sagebrush in any direction. A small cottontail bounded out from underneath one of the bushes. Taking the reins, Lance smiled. He patted the animal's neck. "It's okay, boy. There's nothing out there but some rabbits."

But just as he was about to step up onto the saddle, he heard something. Instinct alerting his senses, he pulled his gun and squatted down behind a clump of tumbleweeds. His pulse hammered in his ears. He still could not see anything. Taking a steadying breath, he rose. He slipped his gun back into its holster. "You've got to stop that," he said to the roan. "You're making me skittish."

He reached over to pet the animal's jaw.

The horse nickered and shied away. His ears flicked.

Lance tugged on the reins. "What the hell's wrong with you?"

Something stirred in the brush.

Again, Lance wheeled around and crouched low. Again, his heart slammed against his chest. He peered through the spiny bushes blocking his view.

Across the stream, no more than a couple of hundred yards down, the bushes stirred. Twigs snapped. Hoofbeats crunched the newly fallen snow. Bulky, undefined shapes moved into view. A whinny sounded in the distance, followed by another. Horses.

The roan started to answer the call, but Lance jerked the animal's head down. He rubbed the horse's muzzle. "Whoa, boy," he whispered. He raised up. Maybe this was Pogonip's herd. He would like to get another look at that proud beast.

He quieted his breathing. He checked the wind. Barely moving, the current blew against his face. Good. It would not carry his scent to the animals.

A few seconds passed, and he heard a horse snort.

He remained still, out of sight.

After a long stretch of silence a small band of mustangs came into view. They stopped, hesitated at the water's edge, then slowly, one by one, moved up and started to drink.

Lance counted at least twenty. Most were brush-tails, but some looked like prime stock. Probably from the Triple-T. Another horse caught his attention. This one sported a saddle. The rented mare from the livery in Reno.

He glanced at the rope on his saddle. Could he catch her? He had already had to pay for her, so by rights she belonged to him. Taking the roan's lead, he quietly lead him back a distance and tied him off to a thick limb of greasebrush.

"Now, you be real good and wait right here." He grabbed the lasso, then made his way back to where he had seen the herd.

By the time he had gotten back, the band had come in a little closer. He would have to cross the creek farther upwind, then double back to the group of horses on the other side.

He looked around. Where was the Appaloosa? He knew that stallion had to be around somewhere. This was definitely his harem, but the animal was nowhere to be seen.

Remembering their first meeting, Lance felt the hairs on his neck stir. He spun around. Nothing. His body went lax. He groaned. Nothing like scaring yourself, Lance. He looked back at the herd. They were still drinking contentedly. His luck was still holding.

He worked his way down a couple of hundred yards from the band, then back up behind them. He checked for the stallion again. The animal was still nowhere in sight. He pulled down his hat, then slipped the loop on his lasso bigger.

It had been a long time since he had done any serious roping. And since he was on foot, he would probably only get one shot at this, so he would have to move in quick before she could get out of his reach. He tugged his gloves tighter and took a deep breath.

He positioned himself behind the horses, putting

them between him and the water. Now the wind would carry his scent. Lance waited for the signal.

The lead mare snorted.

The herd alerted, Lance rushed forward. He swung the lasso hard and fast. He spotted his horse, off to the right but still in the pack. "H'ya—h'ya!" he yelled at the confused animals.

With repeated whistles he circled the lasso overhead. He dodged a big bay charging past him. Snow and ice flew up into his face. High shrills and frightened whinnies sounded in his ears. Hooves flashed. He charged through the band toward the mare.

Apparently bewildered, the animal darted from side to side.

Lance moved in on her. He hurled the lariat and caught her around the neck. She squealed and tossed her head.

Lance wrapped the rope around his left hand and yanked the lead portion with his right. "Whoa there, girl, steady." The horse charged forward, but Lance threw his arms up to scare her back. It worked.

Nostrils flared, she backed a few steps away, then stopped.

"Hey, now. Remember me, ol' girl?"

The animal pricked her ears.

"Yeah. I'm the one you ran away from." Lance grinned. "You remember me now?" Moving toward her, he glanced around. The other horses had dashed off. He could just see their rumps and the snow tossed into the air by their hasty escape.

Coiling the rope as he walked, Lance moved up to the mare.

She sidestepped nervously.

"Whoa, there," he crooned sweetly. "I'm not going to hurt you." He grabbed the reins.

She shied away from his grasp.

Taking the side of the halter, he turned her head toward him and rubbed her muzzle. "I'm not going to hurt you." He moved around and cinched the girth, then patted her neck. She looked all right. He pulled the lasso from around her head, then yanked out a small clump of sagebrush from the stirrup. He stepped up and onto the saddle. He would ride her back and pick up the other horse. "That's a good—"

Another shrill sounded in the distance.

Startled, Lance cocked his head so he could see clearly up the hillside to his left.

A horse charged down the slope.

If it had not been for the black spots standing out on the animal's pale coat, Lance might not have been able to see him against the snow-covered terrain.

In a flurry of white powder and flashing hooves, the Appaloosa that Winter Magic called Pogonip raced down the slope after his harem.

The mare tossed her head and returned the stallion's call. She bolted forward.

"Oh, no, you don't." Lance jerked hard on her bit. Her eyes rolled.

He glanced back at the stallion. "You want to run?" An idea sparked. "We'll run."

With one snap of his wrist he yanked up the lasso, then heeled the horse. The mare leapt into action. He slapped her rump with the coil of rope. He did not know if she could catch the stallion, but it was damn well worth the try.

Once the Appaloosa had descended the slope, he cut an angle toward the herd.

Lance reined the mare in behind him. Lead and rope in one hand, lasso in the other, he whirled the lariat. Urging his mount faster, he closed the space between them.

The mare bore down across the snow.

A length away he pitched the noose. If he could do it once, maybe he could do it again. It missed.

Head pitched low, tail held out, the stallion shot out ahead.

Damn. Lance yanked the rope back for another try. He jabbed the mare's flanks. But the depth of the snow hampered her speed. With Lance's weight holding down her slighter size, she could not match the stallion's flight.

At once all Lance had ever been taught about horses came into play. Leaning down over the horn, he raised his weight off her shoulders. If she was going to get close again, she would need all the power her short body could muster.

As if she understood what he had done, she stretched out and tore up the snowpack. Hooves pounding, ice sailing, she closed the gap.

Lance whipped the lasso overhead. He launched the rope. It looped the stallion's head. He lashed the rope around the pommel. Dug his heels into the stirrups. Jerked back on the rein.

The mare slid to a stop.

The rope snapped taut, nearly jerking the saddle out from under Lance.

The stallion reared.

He pulled harder on the lead, forcing the mare to back up.

Wheeling around, the Appaloosa screamed in rage. It charged forward.

Lance reined the mare out of the way. He yanked the rope tight.

The Appaloosa shook his head and strained against the binding. He twisted and turned. Reared and kicked. He was caught. And *he* knew it. But did not give up without a fight. With one last attempt for freedom he laid his ears back, bared his teeth, and rushed them again.

Quick to remember the last time he had seen this animal gnash at another horse, Lance was ready for him. In one fluid movement he slung the rope over his head and heeled the mare.

She bolted forward just as the stallion made his charge.

He missed her rump by inches.

Lance spun her around to face the Appaloosa again, but the rope had gone slack from the turn and slipped free from the horn. He saw it just in time. He gripped the lariat and wound it around his hand. He braced himself.

It snapped tight, jerking him from his seat. He pitched to the ground with a thud. He groaned.

If the animal noticed the man now thrown from his mount, it only appeared to incite his fury just that much more. Without so much as a stumble in stride, the stallion raced toward the stream.

Lance could do nothing but hang on to the rope and grit his teeth. He was determined to catch this beast—come hell or high— Icy water and gritty dirt slapped his face. Dragged across the shallow stream, he held his breath and dug the toes of his boots into the sand. But it was no use. The animal was too strong for him.

At the edge of the water Pogonip had little trouble climbing the four-foot embankment.

But the snow encumbered his step enough that Lance was able to get to his feet. He scanned the area searching for a tree, a boulder, anything to secure the rope around. But there was nothing with enough substance to hold the strength of the animal.

Cresting the bank, the stallion lunged again.

This time Lance could not hold on to the rope. The water had made his gloves slick, and the rope slipped through his grasp. "Damn!" He watched the animal throw up clods of snow as it tore out across the desert.

From behind, another horse nickered.

Lance wheeled around. He could not believe it. Luck was still with him. The mare had followed. He whistled. He did not know if she was trained to come to that sound, but it was worth a try.

Her ears pricked up. She trotted toward him.

Lance hurried to grab her reins. There was still a chance. She shied away when he bent for the lead, but his determination would not allow her escape. He snatched up the leather straps dangling in the water. After leaping into the saddle, he heeled her flanks, and they were off.

By the time Lance caught up with the stallion again, the animal had already overtaken the herd and was in the lead. Lance whipped the ends of the straps across her withers. Under any other circumstances he would never have hit an animal, but he was not about to let that Appaloosa go.

He leaned forward. The mare stretched out. Aiming straight through the middle of the band, Lance passed the mustangs one by one. For all her petite stature, the mare had more speed than Lance would have believed her capable.

They were just behind the stallion now.

A thought flashed in Lance's mind. How was he going to catch that brushtail? One chance—he had only one chance. And that was next to nothing. He closed the gap.

Leaning down to the mare's neck, he held out his right hand. The lasso draped the stallion's back. Closer and closer. He could almost touch the animal. He would have to be quick. There was no room for error. He knew as soon as the Appaloosa saw them, the beast would wheel away.

Lance held his breath. He was so near now, he almost brushed the stallion with his knee. Hanging on with his legs, he stretched out, felt the rope, and grabbed it.

Instantly the Appaloosa whipped to the side.

But again Lance was too quick. He dallied the rope around the saddlehorn and yanked back. This time he made sure it was tight. He was not about to lose this animal again. With the pressure of his legs around her middle, the mare planted her feet.

Jerked to a stop, the stallion wheeled around. He pawed the air and blared his shrill scream. He fought the rope.

Lance backed up the mare, keeping his hold taut.

Wheeling from one side to the other, it took a few minutes of heavy handling on Lance's part before the Appaloosa settled down enough for Lance to relax his grip even slightly.

Pogonip rolled his eyes and snorted. He stomped the ground.

Lance glared at the animal. For a few moments man and beast remained fixed on each other.

"You want some of me?" Lance grinned wickedly. He barely felt the wet chill shrouding his body. He was too bolstered from the battle. "Fine. You can have me. Just as soon as I run some of the fight out of you." With that, he urged the mare on at a quick pace, forcing the dethroned king to follow behind him.

Exhilaration coursed through Lance's body. He had not lost his touch. He could not help but feel proud of himself. He had not accomplished anything this exciting since before his injury.

Keeping the rope taut, he made for the other horse he had left tied up. The stallion reared back against the rope. Lance pulled him down. "Still feisty, eh?" He chuckled, then heeled the mare to a faster trot. Good. The Appaloosa fought the lead, but Lance held him under control. This Pogonip was a great prize . . . and he had just the person in mind to give him to.

Lance heard the Indian name that Winter Magic had given him shouted even before he rode through the main gate of the Run of the Red Deer Ranch.

"It is Handsome Eye," a man with a rifle called out. "And look! He brings the Pogonip!"

Lance acknowledged the man with a nod. It had been a struggle getting the Appaloosa to the ranch while trying to tow the horse packing the rocker, but he had accomplished it. He looked up at the sign above the entrance painted with three red deer.

A full set of majestic antlers graced each end. Appropriate.

Several large conical bark roundhouses graced the central enclosure where the main party of ranch hands obviously lived. Temporary structures were even now being constructed out of willow and tule for the visiting members of the tribe.

At once a huge group with curious, sun-browned faces left their various games and chores to run and flock around him.

The stallion lunged to the left, then reared his displeasure.

Lance had to flip the rope over his head so as not to be jerked off his mount. "Get back!" He had to fight to hold on to the lead.

Laughing and squealing, the throng pressed backward.

Nighthawk appeared in all his fringed splendor, an eagle-feathered bonnet adorning his head. His eyes danced at the sight of the prancing stallion. "Welcome, my friend, Lance Taggert."

Lance could not so much as offer a *hello*. Even with the long ride to the ranch, the huge animal did not appear to have lost his strength. But the strain on Lance was beginning to take its toll.

Nighthawk signaled for a couple of his men to assist. The two men, dressed in buckskins, ran up and secured the rope from Lance.

"Tie the Pogonip to the post in the empty corral," Nighthawk commanded his men in their native tongue.

Lance tossed another man the lead to the pack-horse, then swung down from the mare. Touching the ground, he nearly collapsed against his saddle.

Nighthawk moved up behind him. He touched his friend's arm. "It is good to see you again."

Lance turned around and greeted the man with a weary smile. "Yeah. Same here."

"I am pleased that you would honor me as I requested."

Lance nodded. "It was nice of you to ask me." He took his hat off and wiped his brow with his forearm. He pointed at the horse carrying the rocker where another crowd of people had gathered and were even now removing the chair. "I brought a present for Yitakam. You think she'll like it?"

They moved over to where the piece of furniture had been set on the snow-covered ground.

Nighthawk ran his hand along the smooth surface of oak. He nodded. "It is a good present. She has always admired the one sitting in front of the mercantile in Reno. She will be most pleased with such a fine gift." He raised his eyes toward the packhorse as if he were searching for something else.

Lance chuckled, his breath expelled in white puffs. He knew Nighthawk was wondering if Lance had brought him anything as well. "You know," Lance started out. He gestured toward the stallion. "That's one helluva lot of animal over there."

"Mm." Nighthawk folded his arms over his chest, then dipped his head noncommittally. He focused his line of vision on the corral, where the men had taken the Pogonip.

"On the way here I told that big son of a bitch that I knew somebody who could take some of the fight out of him."

Nighthawk's gaze swung back to Lance, a glim-

mer of hopeful pride twinkling in his black eyes.
"Did you tell him, also, the name of that somebody?"

Lance laughed. He could see that Nighthawk
already knew the answer to that question. "Nope. I
figured I'd let you do the introductions yourself."

Nighthawk's chest pumped up like a prairie
grouse in search of a mate. "I choose friends well.
They give good gifts."

"Yeah, well, *good friend*." After pulling off his
mud-caked gloves, Lance slung one arm atop
Nighthawk's shoulder. "You got a place where I
can clean up a bit before we show off this new son
of yours?"

"*Pisha'*. Come." He motioned Lance toward a
small round building made of willows. "But Yitakam not have a son. Yitakam give me girl-child."

Lance halted his step. "Well, I'll be a son of a
bitch my damn self." He threw his head back and
laughed, then slapped Nighthawk playfully between the shoulderblades. "I guess I was right after
all."

"Right?" Nighthawk quirked a brow.

Still smiling, Lance whirled around and ambled
back to the horses. He lifted the flap to one of the
saddlebags and reached inside. Feeling the satin
ribbon, his grin broadened. "I forgot. I've got
another present for you."

Winter Magic shook out her white deerskin dress
and held it up. She had not worn it since the Bear
Dance Celebration the previous summer. She
brushed the soft material against her cheek and
inhaled. She loved the smell of the tanned costume.

It always seemed to hold the barest hint of the sagebrush mixed with a sprinkling of dried wild violets that she used to keep the dress from having a stale odor while packed away.

She breathed deeply, grasping the scent of the sagebrush again. It reminded her of Lance. She smiled to herself. He would be coming soon. It had been two days, and already the majority of her people from Coo-yu-ee Pah had arrived.

Nighthawk would present his child to the tribe at sunset, and by evening the celebration would be in full progress. Lance would be there by then. He had said he wanted to stand with Nighthawk.

She frowned. How had he known Yitakam would have a girl child? She chuckled softly. Nighthawk had been surprised with the news of the baby girl himself. He had not been angry, simply surprised.

Winter Magic could not wait to see the babe. But for now only the elder women who had helped Yitakam through the birth were permitted to attend her. Even Winter Magic had been moved into the *kani'* with Moon Dove. It was a smaller replica of her family's roundhouse where visiting friends usually stayed when the bigger home was too full.

She hugged the dress to her chest. She could hardly wait for nightfall. Already the gambling and storytelling had begun, but tonight would be the highlight of the festivities, and she wanted to look her best. She had washed both her hair and body, then bathed again in scented smoke from the burning of dried flower petals. Now all she needed to do was comb her hair and get dressed.

"Tu'madai?" Moon Dove's voice filtered in through the canvas door.

Winter Magic greeted her friend with a smile. Holding the garment against her body, she lifted her head with pride.

"How beautiful, Tu'madai." Moon Dove entered the small house, her blue eyes sparkling like lark-spur. She moved closer and touched the soft cloth. "You're going to wear this tonight?"

"*Pisha'*. It is for only the most special of occa-sions." Winter Magic's face felt all aglow, her heart light.

"Are all births celebrated with such festivities?"

"*Kai*. But this one is different. Yitakam's child is the first to be born here. She is a sign of new life within our new *way* of life. She has brought happi-ness to our people." Winter Magic leaned nearer. "I have heard the old women who tend Yitakam talking. They whisper that Nighthawk has chosen the child's name for just this reason."

Moon Dove's eyes brightened even more.

"She is to be called Bababui Kaiyugut."

"Big Eyes No—uh—I can't figure out the rest."

Winter Magic giggled at her friend's attempt at the name. "Big Eyes Never Cry."

Nodding, Moon Dove smiled. "How lovely." She swept a strand of golden hair from her face, then glanced down at her plain white blouse and black checked skirt. "I'm afraid I didn't know that there was to be such a party, so I didn't bring anything befitting the occasion."

Winter Magic grinned. "I have another. It is not so brightly decorated, and it is of tanned antelope, but I believe it would look very nice with your eyes and hair. Would you like to see it?"

Moon Dove nodded.

Unrolling another hide, Winter Magic lifted a chestnut-colored buckskin dress from its folds. Beaded rows of turquoise stones, porcupine quills, and tiny clamshell disks adorned the front and cuffs. "Do you like it?"

"It's wonderful." Moon Dove beamed with delight but quickly sobered. "Do you think it's appropriate for me to wear such a costume? I mean, I'm only adopted Paiute."

"It will be fine," Winter Magic assured her. She motioned for Moon Dove to turn around. "My people love you. They will be most honored to see you in traditional dress."

Her back to Winter Magic, Moon Dove lifted her hair. "I think I'd like to wear braids, too." She laughed. "Might as well go all the way, don't you think?"

Winter Magic nodded but frowned. She fumbled with the tiny row of buttons on the blouse. "There are so many of these. Laces are much better—more practical."

"But you have buttons on your shirts."

"Not this many," Winter Magic argued, frustration marking her tone.

The women laughed together.

In less than an hour both sat clothed in their buckskin dresses. Moon Dove was brushing the last strokes through the length of Winter Magic's hair.

"Your hair glistens blue-black. It's so shiny."

Winter Magic smiled. She knew Moon Dove spoke the truth. It was her one pride and vanity.

She turned to look at her friend. "You, too, have beautiful hair. I have often heard the women of my people remark that this is so."

Moon Dove's brows drew together. "What's this?" She touched the sore spot on Winter Magic's chin.

Flinching, Winter Magic averted her face. "It is nothing."

"It looks like a burn." Moon Dove pulled her friend's jaw back toward her.

Winter Magic leaned away, but Moon Dove would not relent.

Her eyes rounded. "What have you done to yourself?"

Winter Magic shrugged. She tried to think of a way to explain the mark without lying, but there was none.

"I think I know what that is. I've seen it before." She narrowed her eyes, and her voice lowered. "You've been with a man, haven't you?"

Surprised by her friend's keen awareness, Winter Magic's pulse leapt. What was she to say? She had never lied to her before; could she now? If not, how could she tell her friend what had happened without telling who the man had been?

"Tu'madai?"

Winter Magic pulled her bottom lip between her teeth. She lifted a nervous gaze to Moon Dove.

"Were you with a man?"

"*Pisha'*." She swallowed.

For a moment Moon Dove appeared at a loss for words.

Winter Magic knew she could find none.

They stared at each other, the uncomfortable silence bearing down on them.

"Who is he?" Moon Dove finally asked.

Winter Magic did not answer. She could see that her friend was filled with disbelief. And she would have liked nothing more than to support that disbelief, but she could not. She knew the truth would shine through any lie, so she remained quiet.

"You're worried about him being white, aren't you?"

"You know?" Winter Magic felt queazy. She was quite certain Moon Dove knew the answer, but she had not meant to blurt out support to the question as she had.

Moon Dove touched her face. "Indians don't have beards."

Embarrassment flamed Winter Magic's face.

"Why haven't you told me about him before now?"

Winter Magic stared at her friend, her gaze riveting to the tiny wisps of gold that had escaped the woman's braids. Why was she toying with Winter Magic? It seemed that every question Moon Dove asked caused Winter Magic to retreat within herself more. What were her motives for questioning her? Would she go to Nighthawk with the information? No. Moon Dove was her friend. "I did not know how. I did not think you would understand."

"Do you love him? Does he love you? How long have you been seeing him?" Moon Dove challenged.

Winter Magic thought of the night spent in Lance's arms. She had loved him that night, loved him with a fiery passion she had never known before. But was it truly love or simply desire? She had done nothing but think of him since they had parted. And what of him? That she could not answer. "I have only known him for a short while."

Moon Dove's brows shot up. "How short?"

Winter Magic took a deep breath. This would be the test. "One week."

A gasp escaped Moon Dove, and her face turned red. "Oh, my God, Winter Magic—no!" She shook her head. She closed her eyes, then opened them again. She pinned Winter Magic with an accusing glare. "Tell me it's not who I think it is. Tell me you haven't been so unthinking as to sleep with that man."

Winter Magic blanched. Her lips began to tremble. Tears stung her eyes. She gripped the fringe on her dress with both hands, twisting it nervously. She batted her lashes to stay the tears but to no avail. Never had her friend been so angry with her.

"No, don't!" Moon Dove lifted her hands in a disgusted gesture. "I can see it in your eyes. It *was* him." Nostrils flaring, she took a deep breath. "You slept . . . with Lance Taggert."

14

Crossing the yard with Nighthawk to a small earth-covered house, Lance watched as some laughing boys took turns playing a game of *pa isi'i*. One would roll a wheel on the ground while the others shot at it with arrows. "When will you present your little girl?" Lance asked.

"Tonight, when the sun has set."

"Is there anything about the ceremony that I should know? I mean, what do I have to do? Winter Magic didn't give me any of the specifics."

Nighthawk shrugged. "You will stand beside me. You will be named the child's protector should I die before she is grown."

"You mean I'm going to be the kid's godfather?"

"Godfather?" Nighthawk frowned. "I do not know this word."

"Yeah, well. It means the same thing."

"Then, *pisha'*. You are to be her godfather. It is a great honor to be chosen."

Halting in front of the willow-framed structure, Lance stared at the children shooting at their target. How could he take on a responsibility like that? He could not even get a firm hold on his own life, let alone raise a little girl. He glanced back at Nighthawk. He knew his old friend did not make this gesture lightly. How could he refuse him? It would be a terrible insult.

Nighthawk tipped his head questioningly. "Does this not please you?"

Lance smiled. "Of course it does, Tunupiuts. I'll be happy to be her godfather."

"Good." Nighthawk turned toward the little construction. "But first you must be purified. You must go inside and cleanse your heart."

Lance tensed. He was not sure he liked the sound of *cleansing his heart*. "And just how do I go about doing that?"

Nighthawk grinned. "It is not such a difficult thing." He motioned for one of the boys to come over to him. Then, removing his headdress and shirt, he handed them to the child, instructing him to wait outside the sweathouse until he again emerged. He lifted the flap over the entrance. "Come. The old ones are waiting."

A movement caught Lance's attention. Apparently enraged, a woman flew out of the nearby roundhouse. He hesitated at the entrance. This was no ordinary Indian woman. This one had gold braids dangling over her shoulders. He pulled a face. She looked familiar.

"You know Muha ihovi?" Nighthawk asked.

Moon Dove? Surprised, Lance could only smile. He nodded. So that's why she got so riled the other day. She's the white friend Winter Magic's always talking about. "Wait a minute, Tunupiuts. I want to say hello." He crossed the space between them, then doffed his hat. "Mrs. Samuels?"

Blue eyes stabbed into him. She darted a glance behind her, then forced him back a step with the penetration of her stare. Her face turned red. "You!" she snarled. "What in God's name are you doing here?"

Lance blanched. "I was invited."

She narrowed her eyes. "Oh, yes. Winter Magic invited you."

"Actually, Tunupiuts asked me." He felt a wary twinge of irritation. Why was she so angry? Lance looked over the top of her head to the building behind her, then back at her. Obviously Winter Magic had spoken to her about him. "Did she tell you anything about us?"

"Lord, help me," Gretchen Samuels gasped. "You're not even denying it?"

Lance felt the hairs on his arms come to attention. Apparently, Winter Magic had talked to the white woman. But how much had she said?

The children had stopped playing and were watching the two of them.

"Tell me, Lance Taggert. Did you enjoy yourself?"

"What?" He looked back at Nighthawk.

Rigid in his stance, the man's curiosity was definitely becoming alarmed.

"Don't play innocent with me! I know what you did!"

"Lady, you better lower your voice." He had hoped his brusque tone would detour the woman's topic, but she obviously did not care who heard them.

"Don't tell me to lower my—"

He grabbed Gretchen Samuels's arm.

She tried to pull away.

He gripped her tighter. "Look," he said, drawing in a breath as he took in the dangers of the situation that was about to occur. "I'm not real sure what business this is of yours, but if you don't want to cause a messy scene—and I do mean *messy*—you'd better keep it down."

Out of the corner of his eye, he saw Nighthawk approach. "Play along with me."

"I will not—" Realization dawned in her pale eyes and she suddenly smiled. Her posture relaxed. She patted his hand but slipped her arm from his grasp. "Mr. Taggert. It's so good to see you."

Nighthawk stepped up beside them. "You know Lance Taggert?" His gaze fell heavy on both of them.

"*Pisha'*, Tunupiuts." Gretchen Samuels smiled openly. "We met the other day in town." She looked back at Lance, a hint of anger still flashing in her expression. "I helped Mr. Taggert do some shopping."

Nighthawk's eyes crinkled with amusement. "Did you find what you were *shopping* for, my friend?"

"Yeah, well, I need to talk to Mrs.—I mean Muha ihovi about that very thing."

Nighthawk darted a quizzical gaze between the pair.

"It'll only take a couple of minutes." Lance nodded toward the sweathouse. "You go on. I'll be right there."

After another bout of questioning glances, Nighthawk finally relented with a curt nod. "I will wait for you inside."

Once Nighthawk had taken his leave, Lance gestured toward the pine tree on the edge of the yard.

In silence they stalked away from the crowd.

As soon as they were out of earshot, Gretchen flew at him again. "Do you have any idea what you did to that girl?"

"She's not a girl—she's a woman—a beautiful woman. And, yeah, since you seem to know everything already, I admit I made love to her."

Gretchen gasped and her skin color deepened. "You admit it?"

Anger, humiliation, and guilt welled up inside Lance. Who the hell was this woman to interrogate him like this? He set his hands atop his hips and glowered down at her.

She did not back down. "Just exactly what are your intentions? Or have you planned that far in advance? Do you know what's going to happen to her when her people find out?"

"Why? You going to tell them?"

"Do you think I'm an idiot? *I* know what they'll do to her."

"They're not going to do anything. I'm not going to tell them, I don't think Winter Magic will, and you said you're not. How're they going to find out?"

"Good Lord, man. The girl's an innocent. I don't

care how rough and ready she comes off, she hasn't had enough experience with men to shake a stick at." Her words tumbled out of her mouth like an avalanche. "Did it ever occur to you that because of your little fun, the girl might come up pregnant?"

Lance felt as if he had been gut-shot. He had not considered that possibility.

"I can see you haven't. Not that she matters to you one way or the other. After all, she is just an Indian, isn't she?"

"What's that supposed to mean?"

"Only that you're just like your brother. He did the same thing, didn't he?" She seemed to be taking great pleasure in all of this. "You don't care what happens to Winter Magic. And what about what happened to your dead wife? You just want to destroy these poor wretches any way you can."

"Hold it right there, lady." Lance sucked in a breath. He needed the sting of cold pine-sharpened air to clear his head and make sense of her accusations. He knew that the woman was trying to protect Winter Magic, but that did not matter now. She had pushed him too far. "These *wretches*, as you call them, are my friends. And since you don't know me very well, I'll tell you, I don't *destroy* my friends. I don't know how it happened between me and Winter Magic, it just did. I didn't want it to, God knows."

He looked out across the snow-covered ground, toward Turtle Mountain. "Maybe she was right. Maybe the Great Spirit *is* guiding us down some strange path together—I don't know. But however it turns out, know that I take care of *my* responsibilities. If Winter Magic is pregnant . . . she and

I'll handle it—together." He could not believe he was saying this. He had not even thought about it. In his rage it had just rushed out.

"But I thought—"

"Lady, I don't give a damn what you think." He looked back at the sweathouse and at the round building beyond. "If you're done butting into my business, I've got a friend waiting for me. And after that I'm going to see another friend—one that I care for very much."

Narrowing his gaze, he glared down at her. "You have any problems with that, you keep them to yourself. Got it?" He did not wait for a reply. He had to get away from her before he hit something, and he did not want that something to be Gretchen Samuels. Fists bunched, he spun on his heel and left.

He turned and shot one last defiant look toward Gretchen Samuels. She must be a very good friend to Winter Magic, or she would not have been so angry. Still, that did not give her the right to intrude on their privacy.

He thought of how her husband had acted a few nights before when Lance had confronted Eldon in the saloon. Though Gretchen, too, had intruded into his affairs, she was not at all like Garret Samuels. At least she had done so with good intentions. But how long would those good intentions hold her to silence? He cut a glance toward the roundhouse.

How did Winter Magic feel about what had happened between them? He would have liked nothing more than to go and talk to her right then. But chanting male voices rose up through the willow frame. He glanced down toward the entrance of the sweathouse. Nighthawk was waiting inside for him. Lance would have to find another time. Later, he promised himself. After the celebration, when everyone was asleep.

Lance shed his hat and peeled off his shirt, then gave them to the boy patiently holding Nighthawk's clothes. Once inside, he had to wait a minute for his eyes to adjust to the dim haze from a small fire in the center of the dwelling.

Nighthawk gestured for him to take a seat beside him within a ring of four old men—all of whom appeared oblivious to his entrance.

After sitting cross-legged, Lance heard one of them speak to Nighthawk in their native tongue. He did not understand the man's words.

"You must remove the patch," Nighthawk instructed.

"Why?" Lance looked around the room, gauging the stern expressions suddenly focused on him.

"The spirits will not enter your heart if you hide from them."

"What does my patch have to do with that?" Even though his eye did not hurt him much any longer, he had grown accustomed to shielding the discoloration. He was not quite ready to give up its security.

"The eyes are the pathway into the soul. Only in this way can the spirits find their passage."

Lance hesitated. He was not sure he went along with all of this spirit business. And after the day he had had, he sure as hell did not feel like humbling himself in front of a bunch of leathery old men.

Nighthawk's voice shattered the ominous silence. "There is no need to fear, my friend." He swept his hand toward the circle of old ones. "No harm will come to you. At worst, you will be freed of the demons that bind that patch to your heart."

Lance could feel his pulse quicken. He took a breath. Then, with slow deliberate movement, he reached up and untied the black patch. With a challenging glare, he lowered it, then cut a sharp gaze around to look at the faces in the circle.

One nodded in obvious approval, yet all of their expressions remained as stoic as before. After a few moments another of the elders reached into a basket in front of him and lifted a handful of white granules. Reciting a chant, he sprinkled the powder atop the fire, and a huge cloud of smoke shot into the air.

Intoxicatingly sweet, the strong aroma filled Lance's lungs. He flinched, tried to hold his breath, but could not.

The singing began again.

Lance looked at Nighthawk.

Back straight, wrists resting on his knees, his eyes were closed. He appeared to be wavering a bit.

Lance blinked. He suddenly became aware of a slow dance of golden lights moving in and around him. He slammed his eyes shut. What was happening to him? Was it something in the powder the old man had thrown into the fire?

Peeking out beneath slitted lids, he watched as magnificent red shards pulsated from bright nodes, moving over the faces of the men. A strange energy seemed to have enveloped the interior, shifting the patterns of life into fragments of color and images.

Everything appeared more vivid. A rattle held by one of the elders looked as if it were shining with its own inner light. For one brief moment Lance thought he could see his blood racing through his veins.

He felt a surge of exhilaration, both physical and mental. He was no longer tired. He heard a strange noise—the savage shrill of a horse. He turned toward it.

Vibrant blue, the beast appeared. It looked to be far off in the distance, but running toward him. Lightning flashed and Lance could see the animal in its true colors. Pure white, black spots marked its coat. Like a bullet, it lunged forward, its face no longer hidden in the lights. It lowered its head and pawed the earth, kicking a flurry of snow into the air. A sprinkling of starlight, the tiny particles of ice, tingled against his face.

He squinted. He knew this beast, yet did not. One pale eye, one paler still, the animal bore down on Lance. Images floated around him. Tiny red deer, drawings like those of a child, teetered back and forth above the sign of his family's brand.

He knew this could not be real. Lance squeezed his eyes closed. He held his breath and waited. A woman called to him. "Neme?" Was it his own voice he heard?

Opening his eyes, he moved deeper into the spectral lights. She turned to greet him. But it was Winter Magic. He saw himself. She took his hand. The horse came at them, then slowed to a trot, stopping before them. It blew noisily. The lights vanished, as did the images. But as they moved into the void, he could clearly see that all three walked together as one.

Lance's eyes flew wide. His breath caught in a

groan. His muscles jerked. A hand touched his arm. He recoiled, ready for battle.

"You have traveled far, my friend?"

Lance cut a gaze toward the somewhat garbled words. He frowned. His vision was blurred. He rubbed his eyes.

"What have you seen?" Nighthawk's voice drew him back to reality.

Lance stared at him. "Tunupiuts?"

His friend nodded.

"What the hell was that?" Lance could still feel the rapid beating of his heart thudding in his chest.

Nighthawk chuckled. "You had yourself a vision."

"A what?"

"A vision. You have opened your heart to the Great Spirit, and he has shown you your path."

"Path? What path? I didn't see any path." He had spoken to Gretchen Samuels with similar words, but he had not truly believed them. Did he now? "It must have been that stuff the old man threw into—" Lance suddenly realized they were alone in the sweathouse. "Hey. Where'd they all go?"

"You saw them?"

"Of course I saw—" Lance glowered at the man. "Hey. Wait a minute. What's going on here? You know those four old men were sitting in here when we came in. You said so yourself."

Nighthawk nodded. "That is true."

"Then why are you trying to convince me I didn't see them?"

"Until this moment I was not certain you had." He picked up a wooden ladle and dipped it into a bucket of water, then poured it over a small mound of steaming rocks. "Not all who enter can truly see the images of the four winds."

Lance stared at the mound of sizzling stones. It was so hot, his brain felt like it was boiling. Had those always been there? Where was the fire? "What're you talking about? Are you trying to tell me those old men were spirits?"

Nighthawk nodded. "Sent down from the Supreme Being to guide your way." He set the dipper back into the wooden pail. "Tell me, Lance Taggert. What did you see?"

Lance swallowed. "I saw—" His brows drew together as he tried to call together pieces of his dream. A thought sparked within him. He shook his head. "It doesn't matter what I saw." He paused. He needed to choose his words carefully. Nighthawk might think he was crazy for even making the suggestion if he did not. "I have an idea how we can stop the fight that's eventually bound to come between you and my family."

Nighthawk's lips twitched. He looked as though he knew a secret that Lance did not. "And what is this idea?"

"I think our two ranches ought to work together."

Nighthawk's face grew serious.

"Look. The Triple-T breeds nothing but the best stock, right?"

Nighthawk nodded.

"So what if we convince my brother to go into business with us? We'd use a couple of his mares and breed them to the Pogonip?"

"I do not see the purpose."

Lance turned to face him. "The army wants

quality horses that'll hold up under the strain of their needs. Now, the Triple-T has the quality they want, but the animals don't have the stamina that your Pogonip does."

Nighthawk appeared to agree with Lance so far. "Like your people, my family has been here a long time."

Nighthawk quirked a brow. "Not so long as mine."

"Just the same, I know Eldon. He's not about to give into anything. He'll use whatever means he has to, to see your ranch destroyed."

"You speak with truth, yet I do not see how you will convince him to do this thing. He has no need. The army has bought his horses for many years."

"Yeah, but now they're buying yours. If he doesn't do something to stop you, he'll lose everything he's got." Lance rushed on. "And you, my friend, need your ranch as badly as he does if you're to survive. One way or another, the two of you have to come to terms; otherwise . . ." He did not finish. He knew Nighthawk understood the implications.

"And you think you will be able to make him see how this can work? That red and white man can truly come together and live in harmony?"

Lance shrugged. "I don't know." He pursed his lips and thought for a long moment. Eldon would not be an easy sell. The man hated Indians. And right now Lance knew he was not much lower on that same hate list.

ᗯ15ᗧ

Winter Magic waited impatiently within a gathering of maidens just outside the circle of men watching for Nighthawk to come into the huge earth-covered assembly house. The people had feasted early this day, and now outside the yellow glow of daylight had been swallowed up by the dusky shades of nightfall. Sundown marked the time when the tribal leader was to present his daughter to the people.

A heavenly aroma floated up from a huge fire lapping greedily at sagebrush bark and logs in the center of the room. The slow beat of a drum signaled the moment, and someone began to play a flute, another a cocoon rattle. Soon the deeper vibration of a deer-hoof clapper joined the tempo of the music. A chorus of murmurs rallied through the ring of expectant faces.

Winter Magic could feel the excitement stirring within the tribe. It would not be long now.

Dressed in a fine array of bright eagle feathers, Nighthawk made his entrance into the house. He moved to stand in the middle by the fire. "Tonight I make known to each of you my daughter, Big Eyes Never Cry." He spoke in a loud and clear voice. He signaled to someone standing in the shadow of the doorway.

A hush fell upon the people.

Winter Magic held her breath. She had already heard the talk of the Ganoida bui being at the ranch. She smiled a secret smile and watched as Lance walked proudly into the light carrying a tiny bundle. Garbed in traditional buckskin, he appeared even more the warrior she knew to have been sent to them.

Winter Magic felt aglow. She had waited inside the *kaní* until she knew Lance would be with Nighthawk. She would not allow him to see her until this moment. Pride swelled through her breast as their eyes met.

He made no attempt to acknowledge her openly, yet his gaze swept her appearance with obvious pleasure. His gaze took in every detail of her beaded dress.

She, too, looked upon him with gladness. On this very special night of nights he had not worn the patch concealing his injured eye. There seemed to be a new confidence in his stride, and his warm expression held a private meaning just for her.

"I will speak of the child that has been born to my people, a child that has been given to a new time, a new way of life," Nighthawk began again. As he spoke in their native tongue, telling all how the ranch had come to be and what it meant to them, the distinct manner that set him apart from the ordinary flowed like warm honey over the tribe.

Nighthawk had always been a man of many listeners. His people both loved and respected him. One had only to look into the eyes of each and every person present to know this. Even the great chief Winnemucca himself revered Nighthawk.

"The name given to this child holds much power. A power given to all Paiute this day in proof that we will never walk in the shadow of shame or tears again." He took the baby from Lance, then raised her out of the blanket for everyone to see. Lifting her above his head, he walked slowly around the fire until he had stopped again in his previous position. "Behold a new life for a new way of life."

He wrapped the child back in the linen and motioned for Lance to deliver her into the arms of Yitakam sitting within the circle.

After doing as he was instructed, Lance moved to sit with the other young men on the opposite side of the ring. He took his place in front. Sitting cross-legged, he looked up at Nighthawk. But not before he sought and found Winter Magic's gaze again.

"It is important to keep and remember the old ways with the new. We must never forget the old ones from where we came. So all will know and not forget, I will mark the path of this child's beginning and deliver to her the memory of the grandfathers that walked before her." He took a breath. "Tunu-piuts, first son of Numaga, tribal leader of the mighty nation of Coo-yu-ee Pah Paiute, took Yi-takam, third daughter of—"

Winter Magic's gaze slid to Lance. It would take at least an hour, maybe two for Nighthawk to recite the passing of ancestry. She wanted nothing more than to find a quiet place and spend this time with Lance. But that would have to wait until later. She would not break from tradition. To do so would be an insult to Nighthawk and her people. Later after the celebration, when all were sleeping, she would go to him.

Nighthawk finished the recounting of the child's lineage in less time than Winter Magic had anticipated. The sound of the drum signaled for the rest of the festivities to begin.

First, the men danced in praise of a bountiful year. With the next tempo the women rose. Sidestepping to the beat of the music, each in turn made their way around the circle in front of the sleeping baby. Then they would heel-toe up before it and whisper their personal wish for the child.

Upon Winter Magic's turn she wished for the baby to always walk in the sunshine of her parents' love. She smiled at Yitakam, then, keeping to the rhythm, took her place back in the ring of dancers.

Toward the end of the evening the dance of fertility brought forth all of the maidens still as yet unclaimed by a brave. Even the very young of six and seven moved with graceful hip motions around the ring of spectators.

Fingers spread, hands at their sides, they shuffled in a semicircle, then back again, each pivot of the previous direction taking them a few steps farther around the group until a maiden had chosen a male partner. Then they would rush back to the group of dancers with a pretense of being aloof. Sometimes, it signaled a watchful family to a prospective bride-groom, but usually it was just for fun.

Winter Magic kept her eyes downcast, watching the swing of white fringe hanging from her costume as she advanced around the room. She did not need to look up to know where Lance was seated. Their eyes had met almost continually during the progression of the night. She bent down and lightly touched his shoulder, then retook her position.

As he rose to join her, his gaze remained fastened on hers. Facing the opposite direction, he spread his fingers as she had, their palms barely touching.

With the first brush of his skin on hers, liquid fire raced through her body. Her hands moistened. Her heart set up a rapid tempo within her breast. She could not keep her gaze from his, and, it seemed, neither could he from hers.

She glanced over at Nighthawk. He appeared to be lost in heavy conversation with the other tribal leaders. She wet her lips. Her mouth felt dry. Did Lance feel the same as she? She looked up, but someone else caught her eye.

Moon Dove sat with a group of women next to Yitakam and the baby. From across the sweltering room, their stares locked. Winter Magic's face flamed hot. She knew her friend disapproved. But to feel the open anger of Moon Dove's objection now became unbearable. At the last boom of the ending drumbeat, Winter Magic quickly stole across the room and merged into a group of women serving their men hot tea.

Taking two bowls, she filled them, then walked around and silently set them down—one next to

Nighthawk, the other next to Lance. Nighthawk did not appear to notice her presence, but Lance did.

He reached out for the bowl before she could move her hand. Their fingers made contact, igniting an explosion of emotions within Winter Magic.

She froze. She dared not look up. If she had, she would surely have given away the secret of growing passion rising within her. Had he made his touch known to her on purpose? She wet her lips again, then left them parted. It was an unconscious, yet sensual act. She knew he was watching her, but she could not help herself. Had others seen her as well?

The room became unbearably hot. She needed some air. She withdrew from the men, to the only door. She hesitated. She did not want her departure to appear too abrupt or obvious. When she saw that no one looked her way, she lifted the flap and took her leave.

Stepping out into the frostbitten air, she breathed deeply. She heard the snort of a horse coming from one of the nearby corrals. It was the Pogonip. She had not seen him yet. She hurried over to take a look, the soft pad of her moccasined feet sounding loud in the stillness of the night.

Leaning against the fence, she saw the fluid motion of the white animal, clearly outlined by his spots against the snow. He trotted back and forth against the limits of the rope securing him to a post in the center. The animal blew again.

"Greetings, Pogonip," she crooned. "It is I, Winter Magic." She thought of all the time she had come close to catching the magnificent steed. She chuckled. Not so many. He had never truly been in any danger of her rope. He was too fast. Strange.

Even alone, Lance had managed to capture the animal. How?

As if she thought to see the answer, she peered up at the late evening sky and stared at the pale halo shimmering around the full moon. Tiny starlit crystals floated silently down from the heavens. Truly the Great Spirit had delivered the Ganoida bui to them. Feeling suddenly light of heart, she sighed. This night had an enchanted quality about it . . . as if something important was about to happen.

A brisk chill nipped at her body, and she had to huddle within her own embrace for warmth. She could not stay out in the cold any longer. "See you tomorrow, boy." She waved to the stallion.

He whinnied after her as she took her departure.

She looked at the flickering flames coming from the torches on either side of the assembly house. She did not want to go back inside. There were too many people, too many faces crowding in on her. And Lance was in there. She had felt as if her every move were being watched—not only by Lance but others as well. It was too much right now, and she did not wish to have her happy mood spoiled.

Veering away from the loud voices, she made her way to the small house she had been sharing with Moon Dove. She walked inside, then moved to the fire still burning. Her back to the door, she knelt, then folded her arms across her stomach and sat down. She stared into the light.

Why had her friend gotten so angry with her? If Moon Dove only knew how Lance had made her feel—how he still made her feel just by looking at her, surely the woman would understand and be happy for her. Just because Moon Dove did not have any happiness in her own life with the doctor, surely she would not begrudge her friend what she did not have? No, surely not. Yet why was the woman so angry?

Winter Magic was suddenly confused by her own thoughts. How did Lance make her feel? Did they share the same feelings? The dance of the blaze coaxed her memory toward the evening's festivities.

Indistinct images swayed around the floor keeping time to the rhythm with their movements. Light against her skin, Lance's touch melted her insides. She no longer heard the music—no longer heard the voices—only the gentle sound of her breathing merging with his.

She swallowed. Clearly, her mind revealed the emotions that she sought. Lance Taggert had discovered an ache, a purely wanton pain, pulsating from some deep-pitted lonely part of her body, that she herself had never known existed. And now that he had exposed it, she could not seem to find a way to hide it. Every time she even thought of him, he sparked a dangerous, abandoned feeling within her like a raging wildfire unable to be extinguished. Was it the same for him?

The hide over the door whipped up, and someone entered.

Winter Magic blinked. She did not move. She did not have to look to know who stood behind her. She felt his stare, heated, exploring. Temptation suddenly became too great for her. She had to see his face. Standing, she slowly turned around.

* * *

Lance stared at Winter Magic from the entrance of the roundhouse. She confronted him with bold and dark imploring eyes. Fear shadowed her expression, then faded into passion. With the fire behind her, her feet slightly apart, her posture tense, Lance could just see the silhouette of her legs through the white buckskin of her dress.

His gaze traveled up from her matching moccasins, devouring the full length of her delicious form. God help him. She was even more beautiful than he remembered. He read the heated message in her alluring gaze. She was his to do with as he wanted. And he knew what he wanted. This was madness. The sight of her was like a drug. It was dangerous for them to be here like this. What if someone caught them?

She appeared to read his thoughts but did not relent.

The power of his need became too great. It smothered all thought of risk. He could not stand it any longer. He had to have her, make love to her right now.

As if signaled by some unseen cue, they rushed the moment. Their bodies collided softly, and they fell to their knees.

"We must be careful," she whispered against his lips, her voice thick with need.

His only answer came in a deep-throated groan.

Her breasts pushed against his chest. She wrapped a leg around his waist and pulled him nearer. Her hips moved, pressing against his groin in maddening pulsating thrusts. And all the while her hands pulled and tugged at his shirt, doing crazy things to his body as she slid them under the material and touched his skin.

Burying his hands in her hair, he crushed her lips, plunging his tongue deep inside her mouth. His manhood sprang to life, straining against her warmth.

She whimpered softly.

His body ached with the need of her. He could not hold back any longer. They had gone too far. Reaching down, he snatched the beaded sash from around her waist. He moved to the front of her dress and yanked it open. He backed out of the kiss, but only for a moment. His eyes burned into hers.

Dark with desire, her gaze begged him to take her. Fingers clasping behind his neck, legs locked around him, she leaned back, allowing him a view before he took her. Her breasts round and firm jutted up to him.

Thunder pounded in his head and chest. His eyes burned. His breath tore from his lungs. He could think of nothing but the want of her. Quick to act, he seared her throat with the heat of his lips. One hand supporting her back, his fingers fumbled for the tie-strings on his pants.

She gripped his hair and arched into him, pulling him closer still.

He found a nipple and sucked it wholly into his mouth. She tasted fresh, clean, like crushed flowers, and something more. A light womanly taste of musk and sweat.

Once freed of his buckskins, he lifted her above him, then set her down atop him. Sweet pain swallowed him as he inched his way inside of her. He shuddered against the heat of her flesh.

She clung to him, a gasp escaping her throat. Then all at once she began to writhe.

Still on his knees, he thrust himself deeper, then back again. With each stab she met him fully. Each groan met by a moan. Each heartbeat answered by a matching thump, until at last they exploded as one.

Clasping her to him, he shuddered inside her. He felt the moisture of his own sweat mingle with hers, tasted the salty sweetness of her skin as he kissed her temple and gloried in the fulfillment of her need. In that single moment he knew no greater love for a woman. He had lost himself to her, and she to him.

He heard a distant rustling but paid it no mind.

"Komeni Tu'madai!"

Winter Magic winced.

Lance cringed.

They moved as one. She lifted her head. He turned his face. Eyes wide, they looked into the angry, stern expression of Nighthawk.

~ 16 ~

Lance paced back and forth inside the small roundhouse where he and Winter Magic had been discovered. He glared at the hide across the door. He knew two guards stood just outside the opening barring any chance of escape—not that he would take it even if he could get past them. He would not leave without Winter Magic, and there was no way of knowing where Nighthawk had taken her, or what was happening to her. It had been at least two hours since she had been hauled away, and he had heard nothing.

He picked up a small stone from the earthen floor and hurled it at the fire. Tiny embers sprang out of the flames. "Damn it, Tunupiuts. Why didn't you give us a chance to explain?"

Nighthawk had been so angry there had been no reasoning with the man. Yet there was no explanation Lance could give his friend for his behavior. He had simply gotten careless. He should have never let things get out of control like they had with Winter Magic.

The flap rustled across the entrance and Lance turned to meet the intruder.

As earlier, when he had broken in on the couple, Nighthawk glowered at Lance. He let the deerhide fall closed behind him, then strode across the room to face the white man.

Lance squared his shoulders and lifted his head. He had no wish to fight his friend, but if that was what Nighthawk had come in there for, Lance was going to be ready for him.

For a full minute neither man spoke. Their eyes clashed in a war of wills.

"What've you done with Winter Magic?" Lance asked, still frowning.

Nighthawk glanced down at the fire. He did not speak. He took a few steps nearer, then sat cross-legged, the length of his long hair touching the ground as he did so. Slowly his gaze ascended to meet Lance's.

"Tunupiuts—"

The Indian lifted a hand in a gesture of silence. Through flared nostrils he took a deep breath. "Sit, Lance Taggert."

"I don't feel like sitting." After what had happened, did Nighthawk expect Lance to relax and have a congenial conversation? "I want to know what you did with—"

"*You* want to know!" Nighthawk did not shout, but the harsh tone with which he spoke warned Lance that he had better listen. "You are not the one to make demands, my friend. Now—'' Again, he motioned for Lance to sit.

Lance met the man's challenging look with one of his own.

''This will do you no good,'' Nighthawk said when after a few seconds longer Lance still had not relented.

Lance pursed his lips, then nodded. He knew Nighthawk was right. He was in no position to argue. He did as the man instructed. ''What's going to happen to Winter Magic? Where is she?''

''You should be thinking about what is going to happen to you, Lance Taggert.''

''I don't care what happens to me. It's Winter Magic I'm worried about. Tunupiuts, you can't let her be punished. If you've got to hurt somebody, hurt me. I'm the one that caused this to happen.''

''You forced her?'' Nighthawk arched a brow, yet his voice remained low.

Lance hesitated. ''Yeah. I made her. She didn't know what she was doing.'' He straightened his posture. Would his friend believe the lie?

Nighthawk studied the man long and hard. Then, after moments of silent deliberation, he spoke. ''The woman means that much to you?''

''Hell, no! She doesn't mean a damn thing,'' Lance answered too quickly. He did not take time to think. He only knew he had to say—do—whatever it took to ensure that Winter Magic would go unharmed. ''You know how it is with us white men. We see some pretty little Indian girl, and we've just got to have them.'' The words tasted bitter. Never had he thought anything would cause him to speak so venomously.

Nighthawk remained silent. He stared at Lance. He appeared to be measuring the man's worth. "She feels the same as you?"

Lance scowled. "What the hell're you talking about? I just told you that I—"

Nighthawk lifted his head. Anyone with eyes could see he did not believe a word Lance had said.

Lance took a deep breath, then released it in an exasperated sigh. "You're not buying this, are you?"

"It is not the truth?" It was not a question. Nighthawk knew it was a lie. "I have not wanted to speak of your wife. It is not a good thing to speak of the dead. But I believe she will not be angered."

"What's Neme got to do with me and Winter Magic?"

"The daughter of our old shaman did not die so long ago that her people have forgotten what happened to her. Or why." He lifted his hands in a display of the room. "On the other side of the ranch yard in another house much like this, some of the young men speak of her even now. They say that you took another of our women and turned her away from her tribe. Against the law of the people, she took your name and lived at your fire."

Lance did not want to hear this. He knew what had happened to Neme. What good would it do to bring up the past now? He opened his mouth to protest, but Nighthawk kept talking.

"They say that you are a thief of our women's souls. You take them and make pleasures with them, and when you have no more use of them, you throw them out into the night."

"You know that's bullshit." Lance felt his anger rise.

"Do I?"

"You of all people know me, Tunupiuts. We've been friends for as long as I can remember. *You* know I loved Neme." Lance felt a snag in his stomach. It was the first time since his wife's death that he had ever thought of his love for her in the past tense.

Nighthawk nodded. "I believe you did. But what I ask you now is, does Winter Magic also have your love?"

A punch in the gut would not have caused Lance more torment than Tunupiuts' question. Did he love her? Before now he had not considered the thought. Lance fixed his eyes on his friend. He was not sure how to answer. In the very short time that he had known her, he could honestly say he did care for Winter Magic. And yes, he desired her, but love?

"You do not answer, my friend."

"I'm not sure what to say."

"Listen to your heart."

"What?"

Nighthawk thumped his chest with his fist. "Your heart." With a quick jerk he waved his hands over his eyes. "Do you not see with your eyes? Touch with your hands? Think with your brain?"

"Yeah, but—"

"Let your heart tell you what it feels."

"I barely know her—"

"Hmph!" Nighthawk pulled a sour face. "You need a long time for such a thing? I see Yitakam one time—no two—" He held up as many fingers for

Lance to see. "Next time I see her, I take her for my woman."

"It doesn't work that way with whites."

"*Kai*? Has my friend changed so much in these past years? Always before, you know what you want."

Forced to reckon with his own emotions, Lance felt as if he were being tugged from two sides. If he said yes, he would be betraying Neme's memory, if no— "All right, damn it! I guess I do. I don't know what else to call it. When I'm not with her, I'm thinking about her. When I *am* with her, I'm usually frustrated as hell." His chest heaved with the force of the last word.

Though Nighthawk's features remained stern, Lance could see a hint of laughter in his friend's eyes. He dipped his head approvingly. "Then it is so." He reached over and bumped Lance's shoulder with the back of his fist. "It feels good, *kai*?"

"What?" Lance stared at the man in bewilderment. Was Nighthawk crazy? Lance was not sure anything felt good at the moment. He had just been hit with a realization that he had not even known existed. Both he and Winter Magic were facing— God only knew what, and Nighthawk wanted to know if it felt good?

His friend stood.

Lance followed him. "Now what?"

"Now I go to Coo-yu-ee Pah."

"Why?"

"I must talk with the other tribal chiefs—speak to Winnemucca."

"What for?" What the hell was going on? He and Winter Magic were being held prisoner, and Nighthawk was going to see the old chief? It did not make any sense.

"The people here are angry. They say the law has been broken. They say the lawbreakers must be punished."

"Punished?" Lance did not like the implication of his friend's words. He knew what had happened to Neme. He was scared for Winter Magic. And as usual, when anything truly frightened him, he got mad. "You can't let them burn her. Damn it to hell! It's about time this savage *law* of yours was changed! How the hell do you suppose your people and mine are ever going to get along if you stay penned into your heathen ways?" He raked his hands through his hair. He did not have time to think. He had to convince Nighthawk now, and fast.

"There was a time for that law, but not now. It's like I was trying to explain to you in the sweathouse . . . about the Triple-T stock and yours. We've got to find a way to bridge our differences—see the good in each other and make things work. Damn it, Tunupiuts, can't you understand what I'm trying to tell you?"

After another exchange of defiant stares, Nighthawk arched a brow. "*Pisha'*, Lance Taggert. I understand. It is a thought I, too, have come to believe. And that is why I must go. It is the chief and tribal leaders whom I must sway. They are the lawmakers of my people. It will not be easy, but if I do not, there can be no holding back the young men who want to see you dead." He grasped Lance's arm at the elbow in an unmistakable sign of friendship. "I have no wish to see the death of either my good friend or Winter Magic."

"How long will you be gone?"

"Not long, I hope." That said, he turned to leave, but then stopped short and looked back. "I cannot let you go, Lance Taggert."

Lance nodded. "I know."

"But there is a time, I think, when good men must do as their hearts command . . . and cast aside the demands of a bad law." He lifted his knife from its sheath at his waist and flipped it over. Blade in his grasp, he held it out to Lance. "If they come for you, be ready."

Knees bent to her chest, back against the wall, Winter Magic sat listening to the older women who had been left to watch her. They were whispering, and from time to time one or two of them would giggle wickedly.

Tears threatening her composure, Winter Magic banged her head lightly against the conical bark siding of her family's house. Where was Lance? It had been almost two days since they were separated. What had her uncle done with him? She knew she should feel shame and humility for what they had done, but she did not. All she felt was loss. Why had the Great Spirit given her such a gift of love for this man, then taken it away? She had not meant to love him—had not even wanted to love him. Yet from their first meeting, she had been attracted to him.

Another woman entered.

Her heart leapt. Golden braids glowed in the firelight as Moon Dove walked into the room.

"You must leave!" One of the elders railed in their native tongue. She jumped up and waved a hand at the white woman.

"*Kai*. Wait. What harm can it do?" another asked. She cut a sympathetic glance toward Winter Magic. "Let the girl have her friend."

Moon Dove smiled, then dipped her head respectfully. She crossed the room with careful strides. Glancing at the women again, she sat down and embraced her friend. "How're you holding up, Tu'madai? Have they hurt you?"

The tears Winter Magic had been so bravely holding at bay spilled down her cheeks. She clutched the white woman to her breast. "I am unharmed."

"Good." Moon Dove leaned back and examined her face. She brushed the moisture from Winter Magic's cheeks.

"Do you know where Lance is? Or what they've done to him?" Winter Magic had to find out.

Narrowing her eyes, Moon Dove shook her head. "It *is* true, then. You were caught—"

"Muha ihovi, you must tell me. Is Lance all right?"

"I don't know, but I wouldn't be wasting myself worrying about him if I were you." She leaned into Winter Magic's face. Her voice lowered. "Do you know what they're planning on doing to *you*?"

Winter Magic's lips trembled. She nodded. "It is the law."

"And you're just going to sit there and let this happen?"

"What can I do? I knew the risk."

"I can't believe—" Moon Dove shot a nervous

look over her shoulder, then back at Winter Magic. She lowered her voice. "I can't believe you would be so careless. Is this man so important to you that you would risk your own life for one night's pleasure?"

Tormented by her own knowledge of the truth, Winter Magic narrowed her eyes onto her friend and answered the only way that she could. From her heart. "If only for one night, and one night only, *pisha'*. I would risk all that I possess."

Obviously startled, Moon Dove stared at her friend. She appeared to be contemplating Winter Magic's words. When she spoke again, her angry tone had changed to one of regret and frustration. "You're in love with him, aren't you?"

Gripping her elbows across her stomach, Winter Magic could only nod. She had not even had to think. She suddenly knew the purpose the Great Spirit had shown to her. It was a simple thing. To love and be loved by Lance Taggert. They were to show the people of the valley—red and white alike—how easily and quickly they could care for one another, if they would only try.

"And does he love you?"

Eyes downcast, Winter Magic fixed a stare on the tops of her moccasins. "He has not said so, but I believe he feels the same. His touch says he does."

"Oh, Tu'madai." Moon Dove sounded as if she might cry. "Just because a man makes love to a woman, it doesn't necessarily mean he loves her."

Shuddering, Winter Magic hoped it was from the cold, yet knew it was from the reality of her friend's words. She did not want to believe it. She would not! "*Kai*, Muha ihovi. Lance *does* love me—I know he does. He must.'' The latter spilled out in a shaky whimper.

Her brow furrowed, Moon Dove chewed on her bottom lip. She gathered Winter Magic into her arms and hugged her fiercely. "Of course he does.'' Then releasing her embrace, she looked her friend in the eyes. "I tried to leave—to go and get help—but the men wouldn't let me.''

"Tunupiuts would not let you go?'' Winter Magic sniffled softly.

The white woman shook her head. "Tunupiuts isn't here. He went to talk to Winnemucca.''

"Why?''

"The young men are angry that Lance would try to lure you away from the tribe. They know what you've been striving for.''

Winter Magic frowned. She darted a fearful glance toward the old women, the door, and back to Moon Dove. "And still, they wish to see my death?''

Her friend clasped Winter Magic's hands. "They're scared, Tu'madai.''

"Of what? Lance does not wish to harm them.''

"Of change—of themselves for wanting to change but not knowing how. They think you've turned on them. They've heard how quickly you and Lance have grown together, and they just can't see it as a good thing. They're not thinking clearly. That's why Tunupiuts went to see the old chief. If he can get this law changed—''

"*Pisha'*. Tunupiuts will—''

Moon Dove shook her head hopelessly.

"What is it?'' Winter Magic looked deep into her friend's gaze and saw a reflection of true fear. Was it her own? Or did the woman know something she did not? "What is wrong? Has something happened?"

Moon Dove looked away.

"Tell me, Muha ihovi. Tell me."

Wetting her lips, Moon Dove lifted her gaze. She appeared to be searching for just the right words. "One of the young men rode in last night. He had been roughed up pretty bad, from the looks of him."

"How did this happen?"

Moon Dove raised her hands in a helpless gesture. "From what I could understand from his ramblings, I guess he went into Reno and got a little drunk. It seems he was bragging that Lance had caught the Pogonip. He told everyone that now the Paiute would have the better ranch in the valley."

"I do not understand. Others have gone into Reno. They, too, have been known to drink the whiskey and brag. No one hurt them. Why would someone do this now?"

"Not just someone—"

Winter Magic stared at her friend expectantly.

The white woman's eyes became glassy. "It was Eldon Taggert and some of his friends." Tears spilled down her cheeks. "Garret, too."

Winter Magic swallowed. She reached out and touched her friend's hand. "The doctor?"

Sucking in a shame-filled breath, Moon Dove nodded. "That's why the young men wouldn't let me leave. They're afraid of what I might tell him." She blinked away the moisture from her eyes, then shook her head. "But he'd be the last person I'd tell anything."

Winter Magic's heart went out to her friend. The white woman was also a prisoner—one of hatred and humiliation—and from her own husband. "What will happen now?"

"I'm not sure. They're over in one of the other houses. They're doing a lot of talking and yelling." Moon Dove searched her friend's gaze. "It doesn't sound good. They keep mentioning Lance."

"*Kai*. They must not harm him. They must wait for Tunupiuts's return."

All at once loud voices echoed from outside.

The old women hobbled to the doorway and looked out.

The two friends followed with their eyes.

Winter Magic's heart lodged in her throat. She shook her head. Her hands flew to her mouth, and she began to tremble. They were going after Lance. "*Kai—kai!* They cannot—"

"Shh." Moon Dove patted her hand and smiled. "I'll go see. Maybe it's Tunupiuts." But before she had risen and taken one step, two men pushed past the elders and entered the house.

"Has Tunupiuts returned?" Moon Dove asked.

The men brushed by her. Each of them grabbed one of Winter Magic's wrists and jerked her up.

"*Kai!* Let me go!" She struggled. She yanked against their grip.

"Where're you taking her?" Moon Dove called after them.

But they did not hesitate until they got to the doorway. One of them turned back and looked at Moon Dove, his gaze menacing. "She goes to watch the Ganoida bui die."

Half dragged, half carried, Winter Magic was

brought to stand off to the side of a double line of men holding sticks and stones. Their faces were painted.

Her heart pounded. She wanted to scream, but her voice was lodged in her throat. The brightness of the early morning light stabbed her eyes. Terrified, she scanned the hostile faces in front of her, searching for Lance.

Hate-filled eyes turned hard on her. Someone picked up a rock and hurled it at her, hitting her in the chest.

She screamed, but not from the pain—from the fear. She had never seen her people so enraged and out of control. She twisted and squirmed, but she could not break the hold of her captors.

Moon Dove rushed to her side but was shoved away and restrained by a group of women.

Then, from out of the corner of her eye, Winter Magic saw Lance.

Stripped to his waist, he was brought out at gunpoint.

Three men held their rifles on him. With raised fists and angry sneers, the people taunted his every step.

"Lance!" Winter Magic screamed.

From across the yard he found her eyes. "Winter Ma—" The butt of a rifle rammed his back.

He groaned and staggered a step.

"*Kai!*" A torrent of tears flooded Winter Magic's eyes. Her heart lurched. She watched as the men pushed him toward the gauntlet. She could not believe this was happening. It was like a nightmare, and she could not wake up. Frantically she pulled and yanked, but to no avail.

At the edge of the line one of the men holding a weapon on Lance lifted his arms.

The crowd quieted.

He turned to Lance, pointed at him with the rifle barrel, then gestured toward the people lined in front of him.

Winter Magic strained to hear what he said.

"Against our people, you have taken one of our women," he announced in a loud voice, his heavy Paiute words ringing clear in the morning hush. He swept a hand out over the land. "Since your kind have come into this valley, they have brought nothing but sorrow and pain. You take what you want. You give your hate in return. Now. We will give it back."

A roar of jeers rose up, echoing across the ranch.

True fear slithered up Winter Magic's spine. She held her breath. Her gaze shifted between the gauntlet and her lover. Surely the Great Spirit would not allow this to take place.

The young warrior gave the silent command for Lance's release. He met the white man with a challenging glare, then pointed Lance toward the lines. "You will run for your life. At the end of the line, if you still live, we will send you back to your people."

Glowering at the man, Lance smiled wickedly, then nodded. He cut his gaze to the men shaking their sticks at him and goading him nearer. "If I live, huh?"

The younger man grinned.

In the beat of a heart Lance moved. He slammed his fist into the man's face, then backhanded the closest brave in the line.

The people cried out in protest.

Winter Magic gasped. Her gaze riveted on Lance.

He charged forward, a deep-pitted roar tearing from his lungs. A club came down, smashing his cheek. Another slammed the back of his knees. He buckled but stayed on his feet. He raised an arm against an onslaught of hammering sticks.

Panic clawed Winter Magic's throat. She had to help him. She pulled against the grip securing her fast, but the two men held her even tighter and laughed.

Someone kicked Lance in the side. He groaned, fell over, and stumbled halfway down the line.

The yelling grew louder—more hostile. Again and again, they pounded Lance, jabbing, gouging, kicking at him with their feet, sticks, fists, anything that could hurt him.

Blood spilled from his mouth and flowed above his injured eye. He fell against someone in the crowd. They shoved him back into the open. Bruised and battered, fighting his way to the finish, he struggled to remain on his feet.

Horrified, Winter Magic could only watch. Her body felt limp, and she began to cry in earnest. "*Kai—kai*! Oh, Lance, *kai*!" she screamed, but her voice was swallowed into the shrieks and hollers of the tribe.

Weaving from side to side, Lance threw a useless punch. On he staggered.

"Look!"

Winter Magic heard a shout.

Riders were coming.

A tiny measure of hope jolted her pulse. She squinted.

Indian blankets draped the approaching horses.

"Tunupiuts!" she shouted, not knowing for certain but praying. She yanked with all her strength, freeing one hand from her captors. She pointed. "It is Tunupiuts! Tunupiuts!"

Slowly the crowd began to quiet.

The riders charged through the ranch gate.

Relief washed over Winter Magic as her eyes searched out the faces.

Out in front, racing his mount toward the people, Tunupiuts led the small group.

Her gaze sought Lance.

Facedown in the snow, he lay motionless.

She gasped. Squirmed.

The men released her.

Tears burning her eyes, she rushed toward Lance, pushing and shoving past the onlookers.

Tunupiuts got to him first. Leaping down from his horse, her uncle strode to his friend. He fell to his knees and pulled the injured man over to face him.

A blade flashed.

Tunupiuts jumped.

"Get away from me," Lance rasped breathlessly. He braced himself up on an elbow.

"Lance!" Winter Magic slipped in the snow. On hands and knees she crawled to his side.

"You, too." He jabbed the air with the knife he held. Beaten beyond recognition, he glowered at her from a battered face.

"It's me," she whimpered. "Winter Magic." She reached out for him, but it was as if he had never seen her before.

Ready for battle, yet too weak and hurt to defend himself, he recoiled.

From somewhere off to the side, Moon Dove raced up beside them. "Is he all right?" she panted.

Blood splattered his heaving chest.

Moon Dove tried to touch him, but he jerked from her grasp. "Shh. There now," she crooned. "It's all right, Lance. It's Gretchen Samuels."

Lance stared at her.

Slowly she lifted a hand.

He stiffened but allowed her to draw nearer.

"Heat me some water," Moon Dove commanded. "We've got to get him in out of this cold."

Nighthawk gestured to someone in the crowd now gathered around the fallen man.

With skilled hands Moon Dove examined him.

He winced, then coughed. He grabbed his chest, the knife still deadly in his grip.

"Dear God."

"What is it?" Winter Magic asked, yet did not want to know.

"I think he's got some cracked ribs. I can't be sure. They're bruised badly at best." She looked up at Nighthawk. "We've got to get him inside. He's nearly dead now. If we don't, the cold'll surely finish the job."

"Help him!" Nighthawk commanded. He motioned for two men to come forward.

"Get back!" Lance slashed at them.

Tunupiuts held up his hands, signaling the men to stay back.

"Lance, you're hurt." Moon Dove's voice was low. "They're going to—"

"They're not going to come near me." He shot a

savage glare first at Nighthawk, the crowd, then Winter Magic. "Get me my horse."

"Lance." So painful was his hate when he looked at her, Winter Magic felt as if someone were crushing her heart. "I'm coming with you."

"No! You're one of them."

She shook her head. "*Kai*, Lance. I love you." He could not have cut her deeper if he had sliced her with the blade wavering in his hand.

"Love?" He sneered. He glared at Nighthawk. "Yeah. That's what *I* thought."

"You must let us help you, my friend."

"Help?" Lance chuckled, though by his expression it cost him much in pain. "And you think white men are ruthless and cruel." He coughed again and his face contorted. He spit the blood from his mouth.

Someone brought his horse. Another held out his coat.

Nighthawk silently commanded the man to drop the reins next to Lance.

With great effort he pushed himself up from the ground.

Taking the garment, Moon Dove carefully slipped the jacket around Lance's shoulders. "At least let me help you." She tried again.

He did not answer—not even a word of thanks. He just grabbed the lead but slumped against the animal.

Winter Magic leapt to his side. She touched his back.

He stiffened. "Don't!"

Startled, she trembled at the sharpness of his tone. Her hands flew to her mouth. Shaking her head, she backed away from him. Why was he doing this? Did he not believe she loved him?

Lance lifted his foot into the stirrup, then pulled himself onto the saddle. Nudging the horse in the flanks, he slumped forward. He did not even look back as he urged the animal off the ranch and away from Winter Magic's heartbroken sobs.

17

Lance sat in the sitting room of his family's ranch house, propped up on the brocade-velour davenport, a half-empty tumbler of whiskey teetering in his hand. He reached for the decanter on the round table next to him but stopped short when he felt a stab of pain shoot through his rib cage.

"Don't ya think ya've had enough, boy?" Stumpy asked from the arched doorway leading into the parlor from the kitchen.

Lance gazed at him through half-slitted eyes. He picked up the crystal bottle and poured the remaining amber liquid into his glass. "Nope." Gingerly he set the container to its original position and leaned back against some pillows.

"Ye're lookin' mightily shitily." Stumpy wiped his hands on the dish-towel apron tucked into his pants and sauntered into the room. "Why don't you let us get Doc Samuels out here to take a look at you?

271

Them ribs a yers has got to be mightily sore—maybe even—"

"I don't need a doctor," Lance sneered. "Least of all that son of a bitch."

"What do ya have against him? Ya barely know the man—I mean, I heard what happened in the saloon the other day, but is that really enough for ya to hate him like ya do?" Stumpy shook his head. "Hell, boy. Eldon said that when he told the Doc and the rest a his buddies what them Paiutes did to ya, he was madder than a drenched hornet."

Lance raised his brows noncommittally. He couldn't care less how mad any of them were—including Eldon. He had his own anger to consider. He had been doing a lot of thinking about Winter Magic. He did not want to, but he could not help himself. What was happening to her? Was she being punished? Why was he so worried? After what her people did to him? And she was one of them.

The front door opened and someone stomped in on the braided rag rug in the hallway. "Hey, Stumpy?" Shea called out.

"What do ya want?" The old man sounded annoyed.

"What's for lunch? I'm hungry."

Whirling around, Stumpy moved back through the doorway, but not before he tossed a caustic remark aimed at Lance. "Well, at least somebody's got an appetite around here for somethin' other than liquor."

Lance lifted his glass as if to toast the comment. He had not eaten more than a mouthful of food since he had made it home the previous afternoon.

Right now he did not care if he ever ate again. He was in a lot of pain—not just from the beating he had taken, but from deep within. The kind that only numbness could fix.

He thought of Winter Magic again. She had said she loved him. Why? She barely knew him. Sure, they had made love—beautiful, sweet love—but that was purely physical. It had not meant anything. Yet why did he feel so much torment when he thought about her? Damn it! He took another gulp, allowing the fiery liquid to burn its way through him. He did not like feeling this way—or *feeling* at all, for that matter.

He heard Shea's voice again, then Stumpy's in return. He grimaced. He knew they were probably talking about him. Since his arrival from the Indian ranch, he was all they seemed to talk about—and to. Nobody would leave him alone.

He sat up. He had no wish to listen to any of Shea's chastising—not again. It did not seem to bother his younger brother that he had been injured by the Indians. Shea's only concern was with Winter Magic and what was happening to her.

Shea poked his head around the corner, then walked into the room. "Still at it, huh?" He took off his coat and hat, then tossed them onto one of the cushions of a high-backed rocker. He plopped down in a matching straight-legged chair, hooking his knee over the arm as he did so.

Lance pulled one side of his mouth into a sarcastic smirk and poured himself another jolt.

Shea shook his head. "You think that's goin' to help?"

"Has so far," Lance slurred. He had not had

nearly enough whiskey to impair his speech, but he didn't want his brother to know that.

Shea snorted. "So how long you aimin' to sit around here wallowin' in your own self-pity?"

"Wallowing, little brother?" The word did not make him angry, it just made him think. That was what he was doing, was it not?

"Yup, you know. Sittin' around here, feelin' sorry for yourself. Drinkin' yourself into a drunk rag while God only knows what's happenin' to Winter Magic—that kind of wallowin'."

This time Shea's definition *did* make Lance angry. "What do you know about it? And what does Winter Magic have to do with me wallowing in anything?"

"You think I can't guess what happened between you and her? You think I don't know what's *gonna* happen to her without somebody there to protect her?" He glowered at Lance. "Damn it, Lance. Don't you give a shit? Doesn't that woman mean anything to you?"

"You don't know what you're talking about, Shea. You weren't there. You didn't see what happened." Lance slammed down the remaining portion of his drink. He gripped the empty glass and tried to find a more comfortable position.

"I didn't have to be."

"I thought you were hungry." Lance wanted to end his brother's badgering. He had no desire to talk to anyone. Could they not see he was suffering from the bruises and welts?

"I know you love her," Shea announced matter-of-factly.

"What?" Lance cut him a quizzical glare.

"I said—"

"I know what you said. Where the hell did you get that idea?" He shifted again, but still remained restless.

"*You* told me."

"Me?" Lance squinted.

"Yesterday, after you rode in and we got you to bed. You blacked out. That's how I know what happened."

Lance felt himself redden. Was it true? Had he been delirious? He could not remember.

Shea studied his brother a moment before he continued. "You made love to her, didn't you?"

Lance did not answer him. Instead, he looked away. He touched a sore spot beneath the eye patch. He had thought he had lost it, but after searching his coat, he had discovered it wadded up in one of its pockets. He flexed his hand, then rubbed the discolored heel of his palm with the other one.

"It's okay, Lance. You can talk to me. I know how you must feel. I know you must be fightin' yourself like hell right now. It can't be easy to come home from one mess and end up in another. But you know, runnin' just don't seem to help. Somehow the problems you try to run from always seem to have a way of finding you again, don't they?"

"Running? Running from what?" Lance felt the hairs on the back of his neck stand up.

Shea motioned toward the patch. "Well. Your eye for one thing. I know it had to be tough to think you weren't good enough to do your job anymore. It had to be hard on you to come back home. And then, to find yourself in love with another Indian woman—especially seein's how you could lose Winter Magic the same way you did—"

"You don't know shit!"

Shea flinched.

Lance could see his outburst had startled his younger brother. He knew Shea was only trying to help, but it didn't matter. He watched the flecks of brown darken in the man's hazel eyes.

"You know . . . while you were gone, I thought you were the greatest person I had ever known. You never took any guff from anybody—not even Pa. You were out there somewhere"—he gestured toward the outdoors—"chasin' down bad guys, workin' for the governor, and bein' your own man. I looked up to you. Hell, I wanted to be just like you."

Lance swallowed the lump in his throat. He had never known how much he had meant to his younger brother.

Shea stared at him for a long moment, then his lip curled, and his eyes narrowed. "But not anymore. Now I see what you're really like. When things get too tough for you, you jump into a bottle. Hell, Lance. Where's your backbone? You can't tell me that you ran and hid like this every time things got a little rough?"

"Shut your mouth!" Lance lunged to his feet, but his temper cost him in pain. He grabbed his side.

"What? You goin' to get mad now? Then what? Who're you goin' to blame this time?" Shea swung his foot down to the floor and met his brother's challenging posture.

"What's that suppose to mean?"

"It means, Pa isn't here for you to blame for any

of this. You did it all yourself. Hell, Lance. Did you ever think that if you'd stayed home, or had maybe taken Neme and the baby with you, neither of them would be dead now?" He chuckled, though there was no humor in his laughter. "Maybe what Pa told her held more truth than you'd like to admit. Is that it?"

"What truth?" Lance felt his anger mounting.

"That you were ashamed of her, and with your new job and all you really didn't want an Indian squaw and her half-breed baby hangin' around your neck." He cocked his head to one side. "Is that it? You were ashamed of her bein' Indian?"

"You don't know what you're talking about. You were just a kid."

"You don't gotta be grown to figure out—"

"I loved her, damn you!"

"Did you? Then why'd you leave her here all alone? You knew how Pa felt about her."

"I wanted to find us a place to live—so she'd be comfortable."

"So *she'd* be comfortable. Or was it you?"

"You're not making any sense." Lance turned away and moved toward a small mahogany cabinet. He needed another drink, and the decanter was empty. His ribs were starting to hurt worse.

"Why didn't you want Neme to go with you? She could've stayed with you at a hotel—a boardin' house—anywhere. Hell, that woman loved you so much, she'd have even camped out with you on the edge of town."

Lance looked back at Shea. The man just did not understand. "I was afraid she'd be uncomfortable with all the stares and gossip from the prim society women. I wanted to protect her. I wanted her to have her own place, then she'd feel more accepted. Sacramento would've been cruel to a delicate woman like her."

Shea scowled. "A delicate—" He sighed heavily, then looked down at the tops of his boots and shook his head before squinting up at Lance again. "Was that really the reason? Did you truly just want to protect *her*?"

Wide-eyed, Lance stared at the man. He could not find his voice. He wanted to defend his actions—make Shea understand that things were not always as they appeared, but how much truth was actually in what his younger brother had said? Had he really left Neme alone in the valley for her sake—or his?

He had to get out of there. He could not bear to look at his younger brother a minute longer. With encumbered steps he moved to where his hat and jacket hung in the entryway.

"Where're you going?"

Shoving his arm through his coat sleeve, Lance glared back at Shea. "I can't see where that's any of your concern—besides, I thought you were only interested in Winter Magic and what was happening to her."

"Do you hear yourself? You sound like a selfish kid." Shea shook his head, a look of disgust marking his features. "Ain't you tired of feelin' sorry for yourself yet? Ain't you even worried about her?"

Lance could hardly button his coat, his side hurt him so badly, and to have Shea turn such an accusing tone on him only made things worse. Yet his injured pride would not be swallowed back.

"You're so worried," he turned the knob and stepped onto the porch, "you go to her!" That said, he slammed the door behind him.

It took a while, but Lance managed to saddle his mare. He had half expected—half hoped—Shea would come out and bring him back in. But the younger man did not.

After three painful attempts he struggled up and onto his mount. He urged the animal out of the barn keeping a careful check on her gait. He did not know where he was going, he only knew he had to get out of the house and away from his brother's reproach.

Out of the main yard, he let the mare have her head. The frozen terrain became no more than a blur of white. He did not care where he was riding—not until he had been out for nearly an hour and was within a good stone's throw of his parents' graves.

He lifted his gaze and stared up at Ol' Char standing its protective vigil over the little fenced-in cemetery. He gritted his teeth and rolled his eyes heavenward. "Damn it! There's no peace from this anywhere—not even out here."

Reluctantly he stepped down from the horse, then lead her to the picket gate and tied her reins. He looked at the marker at the head of his mother's grave. Funny. He could barely remember her face. But he knew she had been beautiful. He had heard his father say so often enough, especially when the man had been attacked by a bout of melancholy and taken more than a little drink.

He swung the gate open and walked inside. After removing his hat, he knelt between the two headstones. His gaze lovingly traced the mound of snow-covered earth blanketing his mother's remains. He brushed away a small limb that had blown atop the grave.

His gaze flitted to the other headstone. He stiffened. No matter how hard he tried, he could not put that man's face from memory. It haunted his dreams. His throat closed. He could feel the years of anger beginning to surge in his blood.

He narrowed his eyes. "Damn you, Pa! You started all of this. You and that damn hate you had for every Indian you ever laid your eyes on. Why couldn't you just leave well enough alone? None of this would be happening if you had." He gripped the brim of his hat and squeezed.

A chill breeze whispered across his face, and he sneered as if he imagined it to be his father's voice.

"God, what a bastard you were." He bunched his fists. "How could anyone as wonderful as Mother ever love you? Ever since she died, you were filled with nothing but meanness and hate. Nothing anybody did was good enough for you, was it? You'd hound them and badger them, telling us how to do everything, then you'd just turn around and redo whatever it was.

"And when Neme came along, you got worse." He felt his eyes begin to water, but he blamed it on the cold. He was too mad. He would not let himself believe it could be from anything else. "Why did you have to send her away? She never did anything to you. She tried to make you like her, but you wouldn't hear of it, would you? Not the great Timothy Taggert—oh, no! You were too good to have an Indian for a daughter-in-law."

Scalding tears turned cold the instant they met the air and plowed down Lance's jaws. "I hate you, you old bastard. For what you did to me, to Neme, to the baby . . ."

Shea's voice came back to him. *"You sure you weren't the one ashamed of havin' an Indian wife and a half-breed baby?"*

He grimaced. He felt a twinge of pain in his chest, though this time he was unsure whether or not it came from his injury or his conscience. He blinked.

Lance stared at the ground. He felt mean, cold, and useless inside. Just like his father. Shea had been right. How had one man so young and inexperienced realized so much about Lance?

It was true. Everything Shea had said was true. Lance *had* left Neme for his own sake. He had thought to ease her into polite society. He had wanted the job with the governor's office so badly that he had not given consideration to Neme's wants and wishes. He had known she was uncomfortable about going to Sacramento, but it had not swayed him. Then, once he got the job, it had hit him. How would his Indian wife and child be accepted?

With this realization, another stabbed him even harder. *Lance* had been the reason behind Neme and the baby's deaths, not his father. He sucked in a shuddering breath. And now he was willing just to stand by and watch it all take place again?

"Oh, God. Help me." His shoulders slumped and his body shook. "Forgive me, Pa. It wasn't all your fault. I should've been here for her. I should've worked harder to help you accept our love for each other."

He had not cried since he was a little boy—not even when Neme and the baby died. And now he allowed the ministry of salty tears to wash the pain from his soul with complete abandon. His sobs mingled with the murmur of the wind rustling through the branches of Ol' Char. How long he sat there weeping he did not know. He only knew of the many years of self-inflicted torment being released within him. After a while there were no more tears, no more heartache, no more anger, only blessed relief.

In the distance behind him he heard a rider galloping toward him. He turned around and looked. Moisture still blurred his vision. He wiped it away.

"Lance!" It was Shea.

Rising, he swiped his nose with the back of his hand.

Skidding to a halt, Shea shifted in his saddle. "There's really goin' to be trouble out at the Run of the Red Deer now."

"What?"

Shea panted then gulped for air. "Eldon went into town and brought some of his buddies out to the ranch right after you left. They came for rifles. He said that he was going to see that Tunupiuts and his people paid for doing that to you." He gestured toward Lance's injured ribs. "He's real pissed, Lance. And I think he means it."

"He still at the house?"

Shea shook his head. "They just left. He took most of the hands, too." Shea glowered down at his brother. "He's been itchin' for an excuse to go after them, and now he's got one."

Lance stared at Shea. Damn Eldon. Why could he not just leave this alone? He glanced over his shoulder at his father's grave. He had just posed that same question to the man's ghost.

"Lance?"

He looked back at Shea.

"You goin' to do somethin' about this?"

Lance did not answer right away. He was not sure what to do. But Shea was right. He had to do something. This had to end—now.

"Lance? Somebody's got to go after Winter Magic. What if she gets hurt? And the rest of her people— Tunupiuts . . . Yitakam . . . What about them?" He gripped his reins tighter. "Damn it, Lance. You've got to do somethin'! If it was Chloe, I sure as hell wouldn't be sittin' on my butt by some grave-sides feelin' sorry for myself. I know you love Winter Magic. What the hell's wrong with you? You want to see her end up like Neme?"

Stunned, yet angered more, Lance could not find his voice. Shea had plucked a raw nerve, and now it vibrated through the entire length of Lance's being.

Shea shook his head, then snorted. "To hell with you! Don't worry about anythin', big brother. You just stay here and mope. You don't have to lift a finger." Then, without another word, he wheeled his horse around and rode out as quickly as he had come.

Lance stared after him for a minute. Voices echoed in his mind. You love Winter Magic. You know you do. And she loves you. You're not helpless. You used your pain as an excuse to feel sorry for yourself. Be the man you once were. You

can't just hang around and wait for your litt
brother to take care of everything for you.

Shea's statement came back at him. *"Somebody*
got to go after Winter Magic. What if she ge
hurt?"

Winter Magic! Lance's heart jumped to his throa
If Eldon and his men rode down on the Paiute
ranch, people were bound to be killed. Maybe eve
Winter Magic.

If Tunupiuts hasn't had her burned at the stak
yet, his inner voice chided, though it sounde
more like the remembered timbre of his father'
voice.

He gave himself a mental shake. No. Nighthaw
would not allow that to happen. Damn it! Wha
was he doing? How could he stand around cor
templating what had or had not happened whe
the woman he loved was about to be attacked–
and by his own brother? He had to go after her. H
had to get there before it was too late. He could n
allow anything to happen to her. He had lost th
love of one woman to the foolishness of his ow
pride. He would not let the same thing occu
again.

Ignoring the pain that shot through his body, h
slammed his hat down atop his head and lurche
toward the mare. "Shea!" he called out after hi
brother. With a forced effort he struggled atop th
mare. He jerked the horse's head and spun th
animal around. He jabbed her sides with his heels
He would have to hurry. He could not let hi
younger brother or Winter Magic be caught in thi
crossfire . . . not without help.

* * *

Sitting in the center of her family's round-house, Winter Magic rocked herself back and forth beneath the security of a heavy blanket, awaiting the outcome of her punishment. She sniffled. The long minutes had turned into hours, and the hours had stretched into almost a full day since Lance had turned his back on her and ridden off the ranch.

She did not care what happened to her now. She had lost Lance. Let her people burn her; it did not matter.

"Komeni Tu'madai."

Through blurred vision, Winter Magic turned to see her uncle enter the house. Lowering her head, she stood.

"I would speak to you." Nighthawk motioned for her to retake her seat, then he knelt in front of her. "I have been with the other tribal leaders."

Holding her breath, she swallowed. Here it was—her sentence of death. Her people had judged her as doing evil, and she would be punished for it.

"We have talked much. We have talked long." He paused.

Winter Magic squeezed her eyes closed. She tensed. Why did he not just tell her and be done with it? Was this part of the torture she must endure?

"Before I left to go to Coo-yu-ee Pah and speak to Winnemucca, I talked to Lance Taggert."

A shudder rippled through her at the sound of Lance's name.

"I asked him of his feelings for you, Komen Tu'madai."

Her mouth went dry. What was she to say? Hesitantly she looked up from beneath tear-filled lashes. "How did he answer?"

Nighthawk pierced her with a meaningful look. "It is not what he said, but what he did not."

"I do not understand."

"Do you love your Ganoida bui?"

Winter Magic bit her bottom lip. She felt the threat of tears return. Then she suddenly felt angry. Why was her uncle doing this to her? He had heard her profession of love. He had heard Lance scorn her. "It will serve no purpose to answer you. You already know what is in my heart."

Angry words began to tumble from her mouth. "I do not see why you must ask. You know what pain it causes in me. I know I have done wrong in the eyes of our people. I know they wish to punish me. Why do you not simply take me out and put the fire to my body? Is it not enough? Do they wish to see my heart torn from my breast as well?"

"You do not believe you have sinned?" Nighthawk stared at her questioningly.

Winter Magic straightened her posture. Why should she not tell him her thoughts? She was going to die. It could not cause her any more pain than she was to endure. "*Kai*, Tunupiuts. I do not. I *do* love Lance Taggert. There are others among us who have done as we." She pressed her luck and leaned nearer to him. "You know this to be true. You are not deaf. You have heard the gossip."

Nighthawk arched a brow. "You speak with truth, yet these *others* were of our own kind. They did not lie with a white-eye. They spent their secret time away from the eyes of the tribe."

Winter Magic's anger was such that she felt her blood surge through her veins like a river of molten rock. "Because of this, they have less guilt than we?" She looked into the fire and stared past the flames. She could not believe what he was saying. She nodded with the full understanding. "I think I see clearly now. It is not what we have done. It is the shame we have brought in being caught."

Nighthawk's head snapped up. He jumped to his feet.

Winter Magic followed him, her posture a mirror image of his. "It is I who should be filled with shame over the behavior of my people. They talk big. They want to be like the whites—live like the whites—enjoy all that the whites have to give—"

"You would be wise to curb your tongue before you say too much, Komeni Tu'madai."

"Too much?" Winter Magic's chin trembled, though not with fear—with anger. "Why now is the truth too much? Are our people such children that they cannot bear this?"

Nighthawk reared back. His eyes widened.

Winter Magic knew she had pressed him further than any woman had ever thought of doing—further than any *one* person had ever dared—yet she could not stop herself. She had come too far to turn back now.

"When first we came to this valley and began to work this ranch out of nothing, you told me it was good to mix our old ways with the new. I have found this to be true, Uncle. But now I ask you. When do we bring the new in with the old?"

Nighthawk looked as though he was about to protest, but Winter Magic held up a hand.

"It is not the same. We have allowed a little of the white ways to come into our lives, but our lands are changing. If we do not shed more of the old for the new, we will be swallowed up." Tears streamed down her cheeks, yet she could not give in to them. She took a breath and rushed on before common sense took over and caused her to back out. "I do not accept your punishment, Tunupiuts. I will *never* accept this punishment. I love Lance and he loves me—I know he does."

"Komeni Tu'madai!" Nighthawk reached out for her, but she backed away.

Sidestepping him, she moved toward the door then turned around to face him. "If I cannot have both my people and the man I love . . ." She swallowed hard. "I choose the man." She took another step backward.

"Tu'madai?" From behind her Moon Dove's voice snatched her attention.

She jumped. She turned so that she could see both Nighthawk and her friend.

"I heard shouting," Moon Dove said. She looked at Nighthawk. "Did you tell her yet?"

Winter Magic's eyes widened. Fear clutched her throat. She could not believe it. Moon Dove approved of the punishment? She searched the interior for an escape. She could not let them do this to her. Her only hope—the door-opening—loomed behind the white woman.

"Tu'madai." Moon Dove smiled. She held out her arms.

Without thought Winter Magic rushed her. Lunging forward, she pushed her friend aside, shoving her into the wall. Then, pulling the blanket up over her head, she bolted outside.

"Komeni Tu'madai," Nighthawk called after her.

But Winter Magic did not listen. She had to get to Kozo, quickly, before someone saw her.

⚋18⚋

In moments Lance had caught up with his brother.

A smile grew across Shea's boyish features. "Well, it's about time. I wasn't sure you'd be able to catch me, so I kept to a trot."

"You think you're pretty smart, don't you?"

Shea arched a brow, then nodded.

Lance pulled his mouth to one side. "Yeah. I guess you are at that."

"You think she's okay?" Shea asked after they had been riding for a couple of hours.

Lance slowed his animal to a walk. He was beginning to feel his injuries even more so than before. "I don't know. I hope so."

"You really think Eldon would—" He shot a nervous look at Lance. "I mean, he wouldn't really ride down and ambush them, would he?"

Lance hesitated. He had not been around Eldon for many years, but if the behavior he had witnessed from his older brother in the last couple of days was any indication, the odds were good the man would. Lance would have to stop him—no matter what the outcome.

"Lance?"

He shrugged. "You know him better than I do. What do you think?"

"Yup. I guess he would." Shea kept silent for a long while. But soon enough he spoke again. "You think Winter Magic's okay?"

Lance sucked in a frigid breath. "I hope so."

"You don't really think Tunupiuts would let them"—he cut a hesitant look at Lance—"you know—hurt her?"

Lance shrugged. "I'd like to think not. But I just don't know for certain. He might not be able to stop the others in his tribe."

"But he'd try, wouldn't he?"

"Yeah, I think he would. He came to see me before all of this happened."

"Before all what?"

Lance shot his brother a sarcastic glare.

"Oh—yeah." Shea glanced at his brother's side, then suddenly pretended to be interested in a clump of ice-covered sagebrush. But after only a few seconds he looked back. "What did he say?"

"He told me he was going to see Winnemucca. He said that maybe he, too, thought the old law condemning an Indian woman for marrying a white was bad."

"Marrying? You're going to marry Winter Magic?" Shea's eyes rounded.

Lance snorted with a chuckle. "Don't sound surprised. You said I was in love with her yourse Why else do you think I'm out here freezing n butt off and putting up with the torment of th ride?"

Shea grinned.

"Anyway. Tunupiuts got back from seeing th other tribal leaders just before I rode out."

"What'd they all decide?"

"I didn't exactly give him time to tell me."

"So you mean Winter Magic might be okay?"

"Yeah, she might. But I'm not taking th chance—especially with what Eldon and his budd; are planning."

A sound, far off—a gun shot—caught Lance attention.

"What the hell?" Shea pulled up short.

Lance halted beside him. He tipped his head f a better view of the terrain ahead. It took a minu and a good amount of strain before he saw ther But there they were—a gang of at least fifteen ride or more.

Rifles drawn, they were perched atop Turt Mountain. Another shot peeled the air.

As still another resounding crack splintered th silence, Lance followed the aim of their gun barre

Just beyond the bottom of the mountain, a lo rider raced from the north toward the backside the hill.

He squinted. Who was it? His gaze darted back the group of men.

"Damn! That's Eldon up there!" Shea yelled. H grabbed his field glasses and took another look.

Lance squinted at the lone person chargir

around the mountain. He could tell by the way the rider sat the horse that it was not a man. Adrenaline shot through his bloodstream. He knew that big bay.

"Oh, God—no!" Shea shoved the binoculars back into his saddlebags. "Lance. They're after Winter Magic—"

Even before the younger man had finished his sentence, Lance had heeled his mount into action. Forgetting his ribs, he leaned forward. He lashed the animal with the length of the reins.

Cold bit his face. He lost his hat. Stabbing twigs and deep snow hampered his attack, but he would not let it slow him down. Winter Magic was in trouble. If he didn't hurry, she might be killed.

Suddenly, all around him, shots rang out from above. He drew his pistol and fired. Too far—they were out of range. He pushed the animal faster. Winter Magic was only a few yards ahead of him now. "Get to the cabin!"

His command startled her. She slowed, but another shot—one that sent a flurry of white powder up next to her—spurred her forward again.

Lance bore down on her flanks. They charged into the yard. Snatching his rifle from its case, he dived spread-eagle across from his horse to hers. He buffeted her body with his, knocking them both to the ground. They landed with a heavy groan. Lance felt as if he had just been stabbed. He shoved the pain from his mind. Still clutching Winter Magic, he rolled them behind a rusted and battered watering trough. He moaned again.

"Lance! You are hurt!"

Lance shook his head. "Never mind me. Can you get inside the house?"

"*Kai*! Not without you."

He glanced up at the men. "You got a gun?"

She shook her head, fear glazing her eyes.

"Take this," he commanded, handing her his Colt.

Looking at the weapon, she hesitated. Tiny clouds of white puffed out from her mouth, marking her panic. Bullets whizzed all around them.

"Shoot!"

She winced. Wood splintered above her head. She lifted the barrel and fired.

Lance cocked the lever of his rifle and aimed.

From nearby a shot rang loud.

He glanced toward the sound.

Beside the cabin Shea stood blazing his weapon up at the riders. Their eyes met. "Get her inside." Shea gestured toward the cabin with the barrel of his Winchester.

Lance nudged Winter Magic. He grabbed her arm. Together they raced for the door.

Shea stepped out from the building. Still holding the reins of his horse, he lifted his rifle and pumped the lever.

Gunfire cracked above their heads. They hit the door with a resounding thump. The wood crashed open, and they fell to the floor.

Stars splintered Lance's head. Pain punctured his side. He pulled his coat open and looked down. Blood oozed into his shirt. He glanced up.

Horror marked Winter Magic's expression. "*Kai*, Lance, *kai*! You're bleeding."

More gunfire grappled Lance to reality. He did

not have time to feel the pain. Shea was caught outside. He had to help him. Staggering to his feet, he fell hard against a wall. He yanked off the bar over the shutters, then whipped one open.

Winter Magic flew to his side. "Let me help you."

Panting heavily, Lance motioned toward the other window. "Get over there and start shooting!"

Touching his side, she shook her head, tears streaming down her cheeks.

With blood-smeared fingers he clutched her face. Staring into her eyes, he felt light-headed. He shook it off. "We've got to help Shea." He smiled weakly. "Okay?"

She appeared to understand but looked down at his shirt again.

"I'm okay." He nudged her away from him. Then, turning his back on her, he smashed the glass and started firing again. "Shea! C'mon!"

Instantly the younger man dashed through the open door. He whirled around and kicked it closed. "There's more comin'!" he shouted, out of breath. He moved to the window where Lance stood. He gestured to the north with a nod. "Over there."

A bullet pinged near Lance's face as he gazed out. He ducked and fired another round of shots up at the men, who were rapidly making their descent. He looked out again.

In the distance he could just make out a larger group of riders kicking up a flurry of snow. "Damn it! We'll never hold this many off." He frowned at Shea. "I can't believe El's doing this. He's got to know we're in here. What the hell does he want?"

Shea cut a gaze toward Winter Magic.

"Uh-uh."

"He's wanted her from the first time he saw her. Why do you think he was so pissed when he saw the two—" Shea halted his firing for a second. His eyes found Lance's wound. "You've been hit?"

Lance shook his head. "It's my ribs. I think I broke one this time."

More shots.

"Shit! How're we goin' to get outta this?"

Lance looked first at Shea, then Winter Magic and back at his brother. He shook his head, disheartened.

Shea held his stare. His eyes narrowed as Lance's unvoiced answer apparently seized him. "Like hell!"

"I'm out of bullets!" Winter Magic shouted above the noise.

Lance snatched off his gunbelt, then tossed it to her. His brother's denial jolted him with a surge of newfound energy. Shea was right. They were not going down without a good fight.

Beyond the walls of the cabin more shots rang out—too many for the amount of men that rode with Eldon. Lance peeked out. His eyes widened. "It's Tunupiuts!"

Winter Magic stopped midaction as she shoved another bullet into the chamber of the Colt. Nighthawk had come after her. Shocked, she peered up at Lance.

"He's brought some of his men."

"*Kai*, Lance, you cannot let them take me back."

Lance looked out the opening. He did not appear hopeful.

She rushed to his side just in time to see one of the

men riding with Eldon Taggert fall out from behind a boulder. She watched her uncle.

He and his men were shooting at the group led by Eldon Taggert. Could she have been wrong? Could he have come after her for a reason other than to take her back? Or was he merely protecting her from one death only to lead her to another?

She leaned into Lance. She felt the wet warmth soaking through his shirt, reminding her of his wound. He slumped against her. Turning him around, she tried to support him, but his weight was too much. "Lance!"

Shea whirled around, his rifle still smoking. He reached out for his brother, barely catching the man as he slipped to the floor. He glanced at Winter Magic. "We've got to get him outta here."

Pulling her bottom lip between her teeth, she cut her gaze toward the door. They had only one way to escape, and it was barred by spraying bullets and angry men.

Suddenly all went quiet. She lifted a fearful gaze to Shea. "What—"

He raised his hand, signaling her to silence. Drawing his pistol from its holster, he cocked the hammer and rose.

"Komeni Tu'madai." Nighthawk shattered the stillness.

She watched Shea for any sign of alarm.

He looked out. His eyes narrowed, then widened. His lips spread into a thin smile, and he reholstered his gun. He squatted next to Lance and gripped him under his arms.

Lance looked up. "What's going on?"

"We're gettin' outta here and you to a doctor."

Winter Magic gasped. "But Tunupiuts—"

Lance pulled away from his brother's grip. "We can't let them take her."

The door creaked open.

Lance lifted his gun.

A shadow moved across the room, and Nighthawk strode in past the door. He rushed toward Winter Magic and the men. "You are hurt?"

She shook her head. "*Kai.* It is Lance."

"He is shot?"

"No." Shea answered this time. "It's his ribs. I think one's broken."

Nighthawk unbuttoned Lance's shirt and looked inside. He nodded. "Mm. I will get some men to help him." He stood, but before he could move toward the door, Winter Magic leapt to her feet.

"*Kai!* You will not touch him. Your men tried to kill him once." She placed herself between Lance and her uncle, then raised the Colt and pulled back the hammer. "I will not let them near him again."

Tunupiuts smiled reassuringly. "There is no need for the weapon. No harm will come to the Ganoida bui."

Winter Magic frowned. Could she trust him? "But you have come after me."

"*Pisha'.*"

Shea stood up beside her. He touched her arm.

She shook his hand away and squared her shoulders. She did not need his help. No one was going to take her back. No one was going to harm Lance. "I will not be punished for loving this man," she announced in a loud clear voice.

Nighthawk's expression grew serious. He nodded. "I would have told you this myself if you had not run away."

"What is that you said?" Could she have heard him correctly?

"I spoke with the tribal elders, with Winnemucca, and the people. You were right. It is a bad law not to allow our blood to mingle with the whites'. We must try to work and live together here in the valley. Only then will we walk with pride once more."

Shea bent down and helped Lance stand.

"Let us go out. Muha ihovi is with us. She will care for the Ganoida bui. We will take him back to our ranch."

As if suddenly cued by the sound of her name, Moon Dove rushed into the cabin. Her eyes searched the dimness. "Tu'madai." She darted to Winter Magic's side and hugged her fiercely.

Winter Magic felt the gun slip from her grasp as Shea took it and carefully lowered the hammer back into place. She lifted her arms around her friend's neck and began to weep. "I thought you were on my uncle's side. I thought you wished to see me punished. I thought—"

"It doesn't matter." Moon Dove brushed aside the errant strands of black hair webbing the side of Winter Magic's face. "You're all right now, and we're not going to let anything or anyone hurt you." She looked back at Nighthawk as if asking for his agreement.

He dipped his head.

Shea and Lance started to move toward the door. Winter Magic broke her grasp from Moon Dove and flew to his side. "I will help him." She smiled into one pale gray eye.

Together they walked out into the brilliance of the afternoon light.

Winter Magic shuddered. Her gaze shot out across the snow.

Facedown, red seeping from under him into the white blanket covering the ground, lay Eldon Taggert. He did not move.

Shea bolted to the man. He lifted a pained expression, his tormented eyes searching Lance's face. He swallowed. "He's dead."

Winter Magic felt Lance's body tense, then grow limp. He bowed his head for one brief moment, then lifted it again, a mark of realization reining his features. "He just couldn't leave things alone. He just had to be like Pa—and now he is. He didn't even give me a chance to talk to him about my plan. I could've made him understand if he'd let me."

"Gretchen." A wounded man sat against a boulder. He raised a hand out to the white woman. His other shoulder bled from a bullet wound.

Lance's body grew taut. He appeared to find some hidden strength within him. He scowled. Lowering his arm from Winter Magic's shoulder, he trudged across the expanse between them, pain marking his movements. "You bastard." The words slid out between Lance's clenched teeth.

Garret Samuels looked up from tortured eyes. "We didn't know it was you in there with her, Lance, I swear it. We just wanted the woman."

"Why?" Lance gripped a handful of the man's hair. He snatched the doctor's head up so that he had to look him in the eye.

"If we killed her—the rest of her people—would go back to the reservation." He panted heavily.

Lance pulled his gun. He cocked the hammer. "I ought to—"

Moon Dove brushed past the others to stand in front of her husband. "Don't, Lance!"

"You want him to live?" Lance sneered. He released the man from his grasp.

Taking a deep breath, Moon Dove nodded. "Yes."

Shaking like a frightened child, Garret Samuels smiled. "Oh, honey. I'm so glad to see you. I thought these Indians might have killed you."

"You came for me?"

"Why, of course I did." He appeared shocked by her question. "I'm your husband. I love you."

"Love me?" A look of disgust marked Moon Dove's features. "You haven't loved me for a very long time. Not since the Maidu rescued me from the Bannock and brought me back to you."

"Gretchen!" He cast a humiliated glance toward the others around him. "We don't have to talk about this right now." He looked down at his shoulder, then held up a hand smeared with red. "I'm bleeding."

Moon Dove narrowed her eyes and shook her head. "That's all you care about, isn't it? Yourself and what others think of you? The oh-so-big-important Dr. Garret Samuels. How sorry you must've made your friends feel that your wife had been captured by Indians."

"Gretchen!" he grated, yet displayed a nervous smile. "There's no need—"

"To what?" She put her hands on her hips. "To

say out loud what you've been condemning me for
these past years? Those Bannock were less cruel
than you've been. They may've beat me up a little,
but they didn't batter my mind like you have."

"Gretchen, please. I never meant to—" His eyes
were begging her for silence.

"You never did anything you didn't mean to do,
Garret." Her words slid out with a sneer.

Winter Magic stared at her friend. She could not
believe the woman was saying all of this. Although
Moon Dove had never discussed her husband's
rejection of her, Winter Magic had secretly known
of the white woman's humiliation. And now it was
out.

"Those Indians never touched me—not like you
thought they did anyway. And the Maidu were
nothing but good to me. They're my friends—no
less friends than Winter Magic and Tunupiuts
here." She stiffened her spine. "You call them
savage—heathens? *You're* worse than any of them.
They've never judged me. They didn't care about
anything but who I am and how I am toward them.
They're loving and kind—" She started to tremble.

Winter Magic could see her friend's pain. It hurt
her to watch Moon Dove endure these words, but
they had gone too long unsaid. Once spoken, Winter Magic knew the torture would be over.

"Gretchen!"

She turned to look at Lance. "I want him taken
into town and turned over to the sheriff."

"You can't mean that. I'm your husband, for
pity's sake." There were real tears in the doctor's
eyes.

"Pity's got very little to do with us, Garret. And

as for being my husband . . . You know as well as I that we don't share anything but a house anymore."

"But I love you."

Moon Dove shook her head. "But *I* don't love you—I haven't for a very long time."

He reached out to her again. "Gretchen, please."

Lifting her head, she sidestepped his grasp.

Nighthawk signaled two of his men to take the doctor and the other gang members away.

"You can't let them do this to me!" he shouted as the Indians tied his hands behind him, then shoved him up onto his saddle.

After he had replaced his weapon in its holster, Lance staggered over to where Winter Magic stood. He carefully hoisted his arm over her shoulder.

She clung to him, enjoying the sweet warmth of his nearness. "We should have Moon Dove look at that."

He nodded. "She needs a few minutes first."

Together they watched as Nighthawk's men rode out with Garret Samuels. Shea and the Indian leader lifted Eldon from the ground and laid him gently across a horse.

Moon Dove returned to her mount to retrieve her husband's medical bag, then looked at Lance. "I'll need something to bind your chest."

"There's an extra shirt in my saddlebags," Lance called out. He gestured toward the mare with a nod.

After reaching inside, Moon Dove turned around, a paper-wrapped package in her hand, a puzzled look on her face. "Is this it?"

Seeing the parcel, Lance chuckled, then groaned from his action. "No, the other side."

Winter Magic helped him to sit on a nearby boulder. "What is that, Lance? Is it something bad?"

"It was a present."

Her eyes twinkled. Had he brought her something? "For who?"

Holding his side, he reached up with his other hand and caressed her cheek. "For someone I thought was in need of a particular gift."

"Was? This person does not need it now?"

Lance flicked a languid gaze down over the front of her coat. He pursed his lips, then shook his head. "Nope. Not now. Not ever—at least around me she doesn't."

So it had been for her. Though she was curious, she was more worried about him. For now she would let the matter drop. She watched as Moon Dove replaced the bundle, then moved to the other side of the horse. She would have to remember to ask him about it again later.

When she looked back at Lance, he was staring at her. She frowned. "What is it? Does the pain grow worse?"

He smiled down on her, his gaze washing over her with love. "I guess your Great Spirit was wrong after all."

She scowled. "I do not understand. How was he wrong?"

Leaning forward, Lance nuzzled her ear. "He chose the wrong one of us to be his warrior."

She lifted an expression too happy for words. Her arms and legs, her entire body felt tired, yet full of life. Her heart did crazy things within her breast. They had endured much this day but gained an immeasurable triumph. They had delivered the valley from a bloody fate. Now they could bring their two ranches together and teach them to live in peace.

She caressed his unshaven jaw with her palm, then slipped her hand up and removed his patch. "I believe it is *you* who are wrong, Ganoida bui. Both the Great Spirit and *I* have chosen well. For this valley, our people, the Great Spirit, and for myself, there has been only one warrior." She kissed him softly, then leaned back, her gaze shifting between the two pale shades of his eyes. "And that, my beloved . . . is you."

EPILOGUE

In the barn, standing outside a stall filled with clean hay, Lance slipped his arms around Winter Magic's sides and gripped the rail. He nuzzled the back of her head and breathed in the soft, clean scent of her hair. "It's been a long time coming," he murmured. He leaned nearer and watched as one of the Triple-T's finest mares made herself more comfortable in the straw.

"Mm." Winter Magic grasped one of his hands and pulled it around to her waist, hugging his upper arm as she did so. "I never would have believed it possible. Our dream is finally coming true."

The mare grunted, and from the next stall another animal answered with a nervous whinny.

Pogonip raised his head so that only his big brown eyes and spotted ears were visible above the high railing of the adjoining space.

"Hey, big fella." Lance moved over to stand in front of him. He reached out, coaxing the stallion forward.

Pogonip shook his mane but ambled over and leaned his head out above the gate to Lance.

He clutched the bridle and pulled the Appaloosa close enough to stroke his forelock. "You nervous about becoming a papa, big fella?"

The mare snorted, and Pogonip rolled his eyes toward the stall next to his. The horse's withers skittered, and he sidestepped so that the entire length of his body paralleled the gate. Pogonip had never fully released the wild in him, and being this close to a mare about to give birth to his offspring made him appear that much more skittish.

Lance patted the animal's jaw. "It's okay, boy." He stepped back around to Winter Magic and hugged her up again. "What do you think she'll have?"

Winter Magic leaned into him. Crossing one arm over his, she did as before and drew his grasp across her middle, snuggling into him. "It will be nice if she has a son for the Pogonip, but a daughter will be just as welcomed."

The mare rolled back on her side, her abdomen muscles moving just beneath her coat.

Lance tensed. He had worked long and hard for this moment. In a few minutes both the Triple-T and the Run of the Red Deer ranches would finally be united through two years of hard work, and even more friendship. It was time.

"Hey!" Shea called out as he entered the barn. "Did we miss it?"

Lance and Winter Magic turned to see Shea hoist their eighteen-month-old daughter, Lacey, up to sit on his shoulders. Shaking their heads as one, they smiled openly.

Pride swelled through Lance. He held his hands up to his little girl.

Black hair a muss, dark brown eyes sparkling in the lamplight, the toddler thrust out her pudgy little fists. "Poppy!"

"Oh, no, you don't." After walking to the stall, Shea turned to one side so that the child was out of reach. "I hardly ever get to hold my niece. It's my turn now."

Lance chuckled.

"I thought she was asleep," Winter Magic said. "It is late."

"It's a special night, Tu'madai. Let her see it." Lance pressed a kiss to his wife's temple, then stepped up between Winter Magic and his younger brother, his gaze riveting on the groaning animal before him. "After all, both she and this foal are the future we've all worked so hard for. They should get to know each other right off."

Pogonip snorted, then stomped his feet.

Shea laughed softly and nodded toward the Appaloosa. "Kinda reminds me of another prospective papa not too long ago."

"Yeah." Lance smiled.

"Shh. Look." Winter Magic gestured toward the mare with a dip of her head.

Lance felt a tiny shudder ripple through the woman he had fought so hard against wanting, yet even harder to have. He hugged her close, enjoying the sweet sensation of her warmth.

And as all eyes, animal and human alike, turned to watch the small miracle taking place in the bed of straw, Lance feathered his wife's ear with a promise of their own magic. "How would you feel about creating another little miracle of our own?"

Winter Magic's gaze never left the straining mare, yet she stepped nearer, secretly pressing her body into her husband's. "Truly the Great Spirit moves within you, Ganoida bui," she murmured only for him. "Miracle number three . . . coming up."

ACKNOWLEDGMENTS

The author gratefully acknowledges the help of the Crutcher Family, Ned, Wilma, and Hank, of Herlong, California, for their contribution of the Paiute language. The members of P.L.I.T.E., Pyramid Lake Inner Tribal Enterprises; Amy Dansie of the Carson City Museum; Tim Purdy of Susanville, California, for his help with the Maidu genealogy, language, cultures, and the pictorial journals of Sylvester Daniels of 1874–1875; the many volunteers at the Nevada State Historical Society; Mathew Grahn—Tobacco Specialist (John T's, Pipes & Tobaccos) Bakersfield, California; the local Nevada/California band, Steel Breeze, for the inspiration of their original music; and Richard Goddard for his generous gift of stories about the wild mustangs of Honey Lake Valley.

Dear Reader,

The loving people who make up my family, as well as the breathtaking and exciting locale that are the very essence of the Honey Lake Valley, were the inspiration for this novel. Some of the characters are composites from those I know and love. If this read brought them to life vividly enough for you to enjoy a peek into their existence, then I, as a writer, have fulfilled my greatest dream. It is my sincerest hope that you have found a measure of enjoyment from Winter Magic and Lance's story. If so, I would enjoy having you write me at:

P.O. Box 60631
Bakersfield, CA
93386–0631

—Deborah James